Practical Econometrics

First Edition

Paul Turner

Loughborough University

Practical Econometrics

Paul Turner

ISBN 978-1-4477-7573-7

This book is dedicated to my wife Vicki and my daughters Rachel, Catherine and Rosie who I am sure all find econometrics just as fascinating as I do.

Chapter 1: Introduction

This book has developed from econometrics modules that I have taught at the University of Sheffield and Loughborough University over the past decade. During this time I have become aware that there is a qualitative difference between the teaching of econometrics principles and the teaching of economics principles. When teaching economics modules, the best that I can manage is to teach students *about* the topic. The subject matter concerns the theories and, to a lesser extent, the applications of others. In contrast, when teaching econometrics, from the very beginning students learn how to *do* applied economics research. At times this difference makes the teaching and learning of econometrics more difficult but it also makes it ultimately more rewarding for both student and lecturer. With this in mind, I have chosen the title of *Practical Econometrics* for this text. The aim is to enable students to learn how to make use of the tools provided by the applied econometrics literature. This is facilitated by the integration of the software package *I-REG* which can be downloaded from my website. This enables students to replicate the results on their own computers as the module progresses as well as providing the opportunity for them to try out their own ideas and to develop their own data sets.

What should a typical undergraduate know about econometrics by the end of their degree programme? I would suggest that the following topics provide the core motivation for studying the subject.

Students should understand how economics and econometrics are inter-related. This means that they need to understand how economics generates models to be estimated and hypotheses to be tested. Although econometrics can be taught in a purely abstract manner, as a branch of statistical theory, this will only be of interest to a fairly small minority of the undergraduate audience.

Students need to understand the special problems associated with econometric analysis. Issues such as serial correlation, heteroscedasticity and stochastic regressors arise naturally because of the non-experimental nature of the data with which econometricians typically work. Of particular interest here are the numerous difficulties generated by working with time-series data.

Students should be able to perform their own empirical work and to interpret it sensibly from both an economic and statistical point of view. In doing so they should be able to identify statistical problems with their output and to be aware of the implications of such problems for their empirical results.

The first two topics listed above form the core of a typical undergraduate econometrics module. In the past we would often have been forced to content ourselves with these topics alone. However, with the wide availability of computing resources, there is really no longer any excuse to stop here. It is the third topic, the ability to *apply* their knowledge, which offers the most rewards from a study of econometrics and it is this topic which is the focus of this text.

1.1 Structure

This book is organised with a typical undergraduate econometrics module in mind. It assumes that students have completed a preliminary statistics module and that they have knowledge of basic calculus. The material follows a sequential structure starting with a review of basic statistics, proceeding to a discussion of the basic regression model which is followed by a number of chapters on special topics.

Chapters 2 and 3 provide a review of the basic statistics needed for a study of econometrics. While it is assumed that students have already taken an introductory statistics module, it also recognised that many of them will only have a shaky grasp of the principles involved. With that in mind, chapter 2 provides a review of probability theory while chapter 3 considers issues of statistical inference. The aim is to equip students with an understanding of the probabilistic foundations of the econometric models then will go on to consider in subsequent chapters.

Chapters 4 and 5 cover the general linear regression model which provides the core framework for the econometrics literature. The bivariate regression model is discussed in chapter 4 because this provides an intuitive basis for more general models. Chapter 5 then extends the discussion to the multivariate model thus providing a very general framework for the estimation of econometric relationships. The emphasis in this section is on the derivation of the statistical distribution of the regression estimates and the conduct of statistical inference within this framework. This is motivated throughout by the use of applied examples and exercises are provided which allow students to develop their own hands-on experience of estimation and testing.

Chapters 6, 7 and 8 discuss what happens when the assumptions of the Gauss-Markov theorem break down. Chapter 6 considers issues arising from serial correlation, chapter 7 considers heteroscedasticity and chapter 8 considers stochastic regressors. These issues are often presented as statistical problems but can also be thought of as the inevitable consequences of working with non-experimentally generated data. The emphasis here is on understanding how to detect deviations from the Gauss-Markov assumptions, on understanding their implications for the interpretation of estimation results and finally, on methods which can be used to deal with such 'problems'. Again, the discussion uses applied examples throughout and there are exercises supplied which allow students to encounter these issues using real-world data sets.

In chapters 9 and 10 we examine a number of issues which relates specifically to the modelling of time-series data. Chapter 9 considers the modelling of distributed lags or relationships in which the response of one variable to another is spread out over a period of time. This arises naturally when there are costs of adjustment to be taken into account in the decisions of individual agents. In chapter 10 we examine the implications of dealing with non-stationary data (i.e. time-series data which do not have well defined sample moments). This leads naturally to a discussion of the problem of 'spurious' (nonsense) regressions and to the topic of cointegration. It is difficult to do justice to such a vast topic within the space of a single chapter. However, what I attempt to do in this chapter is to give students enough of a flavour of this issue to be able to interpret regression results with non-stationary data sensibly and enough of an understanding to enable them to go on to more advanced modules which treat this topic more thoroughly.

Chapter 11 is something of an outlier from the main themes of the book in that it makes use of a modelling framework which is different from the standard linear regression model. In particular, this chapter is concerned with the estimation of econometric models when the dependent variable is limited to a few discrete values. The model we examine is one in which the dependent variable is binary in nature in that it can only take on the values zero and one. Such models arise when we deal with qualitative data where observations are grouped according to some characteristic. For example, we might have observations which identify whether individuals are employed or unemployed. As this chapter demonstrates, the linear regression model can be misleading in this context, and we therefore need to develop methods specifically to deal with data of this type. In this chapter we discuss models such as *logit* and *probit* approaches which are estimated using the maximum likelihood approach. Again, this is motivated through the use of examples and the software allows students to investigate these models for themselves.

1.2 Notation

For the most part, the notation in this book is based on the suggestions of Abadir and Magnus (2002). The main difference is that I have tried to maintain the use of capital letters to denote random variables and lower case letters to denote their realisations. This choice is motivated by the emphasis on statistical foundations in chapters 2 and 3. Unknown parameters of interest are generally written as Greek characters. Therefore for the bivariate regression model we write:

$$Y_i = \alpha + \beta X_i + u_i \tag{1.1}$$

4

where Y, X and u are random variables indexed by $i = 1, ..., N$. The general index i is used unless this is a specific time-series application in which case we use $t = 1, ..., T$. The parameters of the model are the unknown intercept and slope coefficient which are written α and β. Estimates of these parameters are written as modified versions of the original characters – for example, the OLS estimates are written as $\hat{\alpha}$ and $\hat{\beta}$.

When writing the general linear model, I use Abadir and Magnus's convention of organising the variable subscripts with the number of the observation first and the number of the variable second. For example:

$$Y_i = \beta_1 + \beta_2 X_{i2} + \beta_3 X_{i3} + ... + \beta_k X_{ik} + u_i \tag{1.2}$$

Many textbooks use a different convention and write X_{i2} as $X_{2,i}$. The advantage of the notation used here is that the order of the subscripts is consistent with the row and column subscripts when we come to write the model in matrix form.

Finally, matrices and vectors will generally by written in bold type. For example, the general linear model will be written:

$$\boldsymbol{y} = \boldsymbol{X}\boldsymbol{\beta} + \boldsymbol{u} \tag{1.3}$$

where:

$$\boldsymbol{y} = \begin{bmatrix} Y_1 & Y_2 & \cdots \end{bmatrix} \qquad \boldsymbol{X} = \begin{bmatrix} 1 & X_{12} & \cdots \\ 1 & X_{22} & \cdots \\ \vdots & \vdots & \cdots & \vdots \\ 1 & X_{N2} & \cdots \end{bmatrix}$$

$$\boldsymbol{\beta} = \begin{bmatrix} \beta_1 & \beta_2 & \cdots \end{bmatrix} \qquad \boldsymbol{u} \qquad \cdots$$

1.3 Software

There are a number of different software packages which can be used in conjunction with this book. The software package *I-REG*, which can be downloaded from my website - www.paulecon.co.uk -, will allow the student to replicate most of the examples discussed. However, *I-REG* has limitations and will not handle the more complex problems which can be dealt with using commercial software. Students who are just interested in understanding the basics may find *I-REG* to be sufficient but, at some stage, those who wish to go deeper will need to invest time, effort (and probably some cash) in learning how to use a commercial package. There are some excellent packages on the market including EViews, PC-Give, Stata and numerous others. These may already be provided by the computer services department of your institution but, if not, I would recommend investigating the available packages carefully to see if they meet your needs before buying.

Chapter 2: Probability and the Statistical Foundations of Econometrics

2.1 Probability

The statistical foundations of econometric analysis lie in the theory of probability. Many of you reading this textbook will have already completed an introductory module in statistics in which you will have come across some of the important ideas of probability theory. However, it will be useful to review these ideas before we move on to more advanced topics. If you haven't been introduced to these concepts already, then this chapter will cover the essential ideas you need in order to study econometrics.

Before we begin our discussion of probability, we must first introduce some terminology. The most basic concept of statistical theory is the idea of a *random experiment*. This is an experiment which can be repeated a number of times under essentially similar conditions but whose outcome is uncertain. Consider, for example, the tossing of a coin. This can be repeated any number of times but the outcome of any single coin toss is not known in advance. The set of possible outcomes of a random experiment is known as the *sample space*. In the case of the coin toss the sample space consists of two possibilities – heads or tails. Finally, an *event* is a subset of the sample space which corresponds to a particular outcome e.g. heads or tails in the coin toss experiment.

The coin toss experiment we described in the previous paragraph is an example of a special kind of experiment known as a *Bernoulli trial*. In this kind of experiment the sample space can be reduced to only two possible outcomes which are usually, somewhat arbitrarily, described as 'success' and 'failure'. For example, we might define a heads as a 'success' and tails as 'failure'. However, this is essentially arbitrary because nothing would change if we were to reverse these labels. Bernoulli trials are a special case of a random experiment but a very important special case. This is because many real world applications can be described in these terms and a surprising amount of statistical theory can be developed using this as a basis.

Let us suppose that we conduct a total of n Bernoulli trials and that we observe k successes. We can define the *relative frequency* of successes as k/n. The *probability* of a success in an individual trial can then be defined as the value to which the relative frequency converges as the number of experiments becomes large. In the case of the coin toss experiment we would expect the relative frequency of success (heads) to average out at ½ as the number of experiments increases. Let p denote the probability of success in an individual trial. It therefore follows that, for a Bernoulli trial, the probability of failure is equal to 1-p because the two events (success and failure) constitute the whole of the sample space. Another way of describing this is to say that the two possible events are *exhaustive*. Note also that success and failure are *mutually exclusive events*, i.e. they cannot occur simultaneously.

To illustrate some of the ideas we have introduced, let us consider another simple example. Suppose we have a well shuffled pack of cards. We make a draw from the pack and inspect the card. If the card drawn is a club then we deem the experiment a 'success'. We then return the card and repeat the experiment a large number of times. The probability of drawing a club can then be calculated as the number of successes divided by the number of experiments. Since there are 13 clubs in a pack of 52 cards, it is not hard to see that the probability of drawing a club is equal to ¼ and the probability of drawing another suit is ¾ i.e.

$$p(A) = \frac{1}{4}$$
$$p(B) = 1 - p(A) = \frac{3}{4}$$

(2.1)

where we have defined event A as the drawing of a club and the event B as the drawing of any other suit. The two probabilities defined in equation (2.1) define the *probability distribution function* for an individual Bernoulli trial. That is, they attach a probability to all possible outcomes in the sample space.

Now let us consider another experiment, this time we make two successive draws from the pack (after replacing the card following the initial draw). The sample space now consists of four possible outcomes which can be summarised as $(AA), (AB), (BA), (BB)$. To find the probability distribution function for this experiment we note that the outcomes of each draw are *independent* of each other. That is, the probability of drawing a club on the second draw is not influenced by whether or not a club was drawn in the first draw. It follows that probability of two successive clubs can be calculated as $p(AA)=1/4\times1/4=1/16$, similarly the probability of a club followed by another suit is $p(AB)=1/4\times3/4=3/16$ and in this manner we can construct the probability distribution function as:

$$p(AA)=\frac{1}{4}\times\frac{1}{4}=\frac{1}{16}$$
$$p(AB)=\frac{1}{4}\times\frac{3}{4}=\frac{3}{16}$$
$$p(BA)=\frac{3}{4}\times\frac{1}{4}=\frac{3}{16}$$
$$p(BB)=\frac{3}{4}\times\frac{3}{4}=\frac{9}{16}$$

(2.2)

Note that because the events listed in (2.2) are exhaustive, their probabilities sum to one. Note also that there two different ways in which a single 'success' can be observed. Thus if we are simple interested in the distribution of the number of successes, and the order in which they occur is irrelevant, then we could write the probability distribution function as:

$$p(k=0)=\frac{9}{16}, p(k=1)=\frac{6}{16}, p(k=2)=\frac{1}{16}$$

(2.3)

2.2 Joint, Conditional and Marginal Probabilities

So far we have considered events which are mutually exclusive. However, this will not always be the case. In many situations we will be interested in different aspects of an experiments where the outcome of one aspect does not preclude particular outcomes another aspect. For example, when considering our experiment of drawing a card from a pack let us suppose that we are also interested in whether or not the card drawn is a face card. Note that a card can be both a face card and a club so the two events are not mutually exclusive. Let us define event A as the card drawn being a club, and event C as the card drawn being a face card. A useful relationship between the probabilities is defined by Bayes' Law which can be written as follows:

$$p(A \cap C) = p(A|C)p(C) = p(C|A)p(A) \qquad (2.4)$$

$p(A \cap C)$ is the *joint probability* that the two events occur simultaneously, i.e. the probability that the card drawn is both a club and a face card. $p(A|C)$ is the *conditional probability* that event A occurs given that event C occurs while $p(C)$ is the *marginal probability* that event C occurs. The marginal probability is the probability that the card is a face card irrespective of whether it is a club or another suit. It can be calculated as the sum of the joint probabilities.

An alternative way in which Bayes's Law can be written is in the form $p(A|C) = p(A \cap C) / p(C)$. This shows that the conditional probability is determined as the ratio of the joint probability to the marginal probability. This a convenient form for the calculation of conditional probabilities which is often our objective as economic statisticians or econometricians. Finally we note that the sum of the joint probabilities of an event gives the marginal probability e.g. $p(C) = p(C \cap A) + p(C \cap B)$ and that Bayes' Law is symmetric so that $p(A|C)p(C) = p(C|A)p(A)$.

Suppose we wish to determine the joint probability that the card drawn is both a club and a face card. Now there are three face cards which are also clubs hence the conditional probability that the card drawn is a face card given that it is a club is $p(C|A) = 3/13$ and we already know that the unconditional probability that the card draw is a club is $p(A) = 1/4$. It follows from Bayes' Law that the joint probability is $p(C \cap A) = 3/13 \times 1/4 = 3/52$.

When dealing with more complex situations in which there are multiple events which are not mutually exclusive, it is often useful to represent the probability distribution function in tabular form. To illustrate this we will consider an economic example. Let us suppose we are interested in the behaviour of the Bank of England when setting the interest rate. We assume that it has three options which we will label as follows, Y_1 is the case where the Bank cuts the interest rate, Y_2 is the case where it leaves the interest rate constant and Y_3 is the case where it increases the interest rate. There are also three different states of the economy which might influence this decision, X_1 is the case where inflation is below the Bank's target, X_2 is the case where inflation is equal to the Bank's target (or within its target range) and X_3 is the case where inflation is above the Bank's target. Now suppose we have observed how the Bank behaves over a period of time and determined the following relative frequencies for these events. The results can be set out in tabular form as shown in Figure 2.1.

In Table 2.1, the numbers in the central rectangle represent the joint probability of different events. For example, the joint probability of inflation being too low and the interest rate being cut is equal to $p(X_1 \cap Y_1) = 0.1$ while the probability of inflation being too high and the interest rate being cut is $p(X_3 \cap Y_1) = 0.01$. Once we have determined these joint probabilities then it is straightforward to determine the marginal and conditional probabilities. The marginal probability of an event is the probability that it occurs irrespective of whether other events occur or not. The conditional probability is the probability that an event occurs given that some other event has occurred.

		Inflation too low X_1	Inflation equal to target X_2	Inflation too high X_3	
Cut interest rate	Y_1	0.10	0.10	0.01	0.21
Keep interest rate constant	Y_2	0.08	0.40	0.04	0.52
Increase interest rate	Y_3	0.02	0.10	0.15	0.27
		0.20	0.60	0.20	

Table 2.1: Probability Distribution for Bank of England Interest Rate Decision

Consider first the probability that the interest rate will be cut. This depends on the relationship between the actual rate of inflation and the target rate. There are three possible scenarios which need to be taken into account and the probability of an interest rate cut is different in each. However, because these scenarios are mutually exclusive we can calculate the overall probability of an interest rate cut as the sum of the three joint probabilities as shown in the following equation:

$$p(Y_1) = p(Y_1 \cap X_1) + p(Y_1 \cap X_2) + p(Y_1 \cap X_3)$$
$$= 0.10 + 0.10 + 0.01 = 0.21$$

This equation defines the marginal probability of an interest rate cut. Historically, probabilities of this kind were often written in the margins of the contingency table – hence the term marginal probability. In general, marginal probabilities can be calculated by taking the sum of either the row or column entries of the table. Thus the marginal probabilities of the interest rate being held constant and of it increasing are $p(Y_2) = 0.52$ and $p(Y_3) = 0.27$ which are the row sums of the table. Similarly, the column sums give the probabilities of inflation being below, equal to or above target respectively $p(X_1) = 0.20, p(X_2) = 0.60, p(X_3) = 0.20$. Note that since the events associated with the marginal probabilities are both mutually exclusive and exhaustive, it follows that these row or column entries must sum to one.

As econometricians we are often interested in describing how economic agents behave in response to the state of the economy. Therefore we often wish to compute conditional probabilities. This is relatively straightforward with the information which is given in the table coupled with the application of Bayes' Law. For example, suppose we wish to calculate the probability that the Bank of England will cut the interest rate if inflation is below target. Using Bayes' Law we have:

$$p(Y_1 \mid X_1) = \frac{p(Y_1 \cap X_1)}{p(X_1)} = \frac{0.10}{0.20} = 0.50$$

i.e. there is a 50% chance that the interest rate will be cut when inflation falls below target. Similarly, if we wish to calculate that probability that the interest rate will *not* change, even when inflation is above target, then we can write this as:

$$p(Y_2 \mid X_3) = \frac{p(Y_2 \cap X_3)}{p(X_3)} = \frac{0.04}{0.60} = 0.067$$

Calculation of the other conditional probabilities is left as an exercise for the interested reader.

2.3 The Probability Distribution Function

The random variables we have considered so far fall into the category of *discrete random variables*. This means that the number of possible outcomes for the random experiment is limited. For example, let X be a random variable generated by a Bernoulli trial. The outcomes of such an experiment can only take the values $x=1$ for a success or $x=0$ for a failure. Now suppose we can find a function $p(X=x)$[1] then this function is called the *probability distribution function*. The probability distribution function is important because it can be used to define the *mean* and the *variance* of the distribution in question. Suppose there are $n+1$ possible outcomes, corresponding to $x=0,1,...,n$. The mean, or expected value, of the random variable X can be defined as:

$$\mu_X = E(X) = \sum_{x=0}^{n} p(x)x \qquad (2.5)$$

while the variance, defined as the expected value of the squared deviation of the random variable from its mean, can be written:

$$\sigma_X^2 = E(X-\mu)^2 = \sum_{x=0}^{n} p(x)(X-\mu)^2 \qquad (2.6)$$

---

[1] The function $p(X=x)$ is often abbreviated to $p(x)$.

For example, let X be the number of successes in a set of n Bernoulli trials. This is a random variable which can take on the particular values $x = 0, 1, 2, ..., n$. Such a random variable follows the binomial distribution and has a probability distribution function of the form:

$$p(x) = \frac{n!}{(n-x)!x!} p^x (1-p)^{n-x}$$ (2.7)

The mean of this distribution can be written $\mu_X = E(X) = np$ and the variance can be written $\sigma_X^2 = E(X - E(X))^2 = np(1-p)$. We can also define the *cumulative probability distribution function* or CDF as the function $F(x) = p(X \le x)$. In the case of the binomial distribution we would obtain the CDF by adding the individual probabilities over the range 0 to x. The binomial distribution is interesting in its own right but is also of historical importance. This is because it was the need to develop a method for obtaining approximate values for the binomial probabilities when the value of n is large which led to the development of the *normal* distribution.

As an example, consider again the Bernoulli experiment which involves drawing a card from a pack and in which a 'success' corresponds to drawing a club. If five draws (with replacement) are made then the sample space consists of six alternative outcomes ranging from no successes to all five draws being clubs. We can calculate the probability distribution function using (2.7) and obtain the following result:

Number of Successes = x	Probability $p(X = x)$	Cumulative Probability $p(X \le x)$
0	0.23730	0.23730
1	0.39551	0.63281
2	0.26367	0.89648
3	0.08789	0.98437
4	0.01465	0.99902
5	9.77E-04	1.00000

Table 2.2: Probability Distribution for the Binomial Distribution with n=5 and p= ¼ .

If we plot the probability distribution function given in Table 2.2 as a bar chart then we obtain the graph shown in Figure 2.1. This shows that the probabilities are unevenly distributed. The probabilities attached to lower values of X are rather larger than those for higher values. Thus, the distribution appears to be asymmetric, with large probability values at the lower end and probabilities that decline gradually towards zero at the upper end.

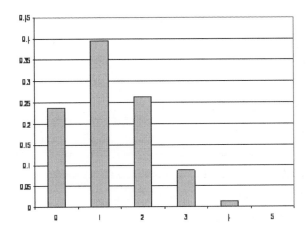

Figure 2.1 PDF for the Binomial Distribution with n=5 and p= ¼

What happens if we increase the number of trials? Figure 2.2 shows the PDFs for binomial distributions with $n=10$ and $n=30$. For $n=10$ the shape remains basically similar to that for $n=5$ with high probabilities for low values and a gradual decline in probability for $x>2$. However, relative to $n=5$, there is already a reduction in the degree of asymmetry of the function. This process continues as we increase the number of trials. When $n=30$ the asymmetry in the function is hardly visible at all. The probability of the number of successes is close to zero when $x=0$, increases to a maximum when $x=7$ and then declines back to 0 as $x \to 30$. In this case however, the function is close to being symmetric around the maximum point.

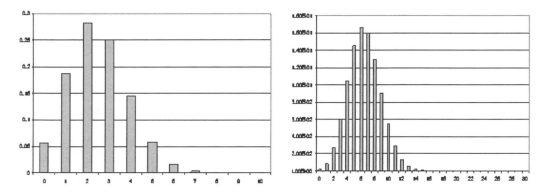

Figure 2.2 PDFs for the Binomial Distribution with p= ¼

The tendency for the CDF to become more symmetric as the number of trials increases is no accident. As the number of trials increases, the shape of the CDF function can be more closely approximated by a continuous function $f(x)$ which eventually converges on the normal distribution. In fact, this is an example of a much more general phenomenon known as the *Central Limit Theorem*. This is an important theorem for statistical theory which shows that whatever is the process determining the probabilities of success in an individual trial, the shape of the distribution of the number of successes will eventually converge on a continuous function which takes the general form given in equation (2.8):

$$f(x) = \frac{1}{\sigma\sqrt{2\pi}} \exp\left(-\frac{(x-\mu)^2}{2\sigma^2}\right)$$

(2.8)

where μ and σ^2 are the mean and the variance of the distribution.

Figure 2.3 shows that (2.8) provides a very close approximation to the PDF for the binomial distribution with $n=30$. The bars in Figure 2.3 show the probabilities of the number of successes from the binomial distribution i.e. $p(X=x)$ from (2.7). The continuous line shows the curve generated by equation (2.8) with $\mu=np$ and $\sigma^2=np(1-p)$. We can see that for any given value of X the normal curve shown by the continuous line is a good approximation to the binomial probabilities. This approximation will continue to improve as we increase the number of trials.

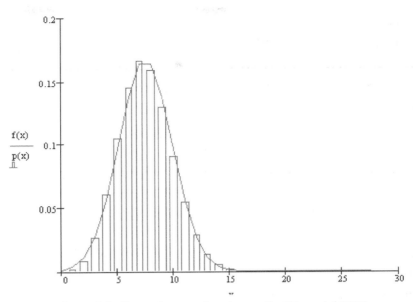

Figure 2.3: Normal approximation to the Binomial PDF

2.4   The Normal Distribution

We have seen that the normal curve (2.8) can be thought of as a continuous curve which gives a good approximation to the binomial probabilities for a large number of trials. However, the normal distribution is also an example of a   general class known as *continuous distributions*. These allow us to calculate probabilities for *continuous random variables*. A continuous random variable is one which can take any real value on some interval. For example, we might wish to measure the temperature in a particular location over a period of time. Alternatively, we might wish to measure the distance between the place of residence and the place of work for an individual. In both these cases the random variable is more naturally thought of as lying somewhere on a continuum of possible values rather than taking one of a discrete number of possibilities.

Now if the random variable X can take on a continuum of values along some range, it makes more sense to think in terms of the probability that X lies between two particular values within that range rather than being equal to a particular point value. This means that instead of thinking in terms of the probability distribution function, which assigns probabilities to particular point values of X, we need to think in terms of the rather more

17

difficult concept of a *probability density function* (which is also usually abbreviated to PDF). The probability density function is a function $f(x)$ which, when integrated with respect to x between two limits a and b, gives the probability that the random variable X lies between these limits. Therefore, if we can find such a function, we can write:

$$p(a \leq X \leq b) = \int_a^b f(x) dx \qquad (2.9)$$

To qualify as a probability density function $f(x)$ must satisfy a number of criteria. Most importantly it must have the properties that $f(x) \geq 0$ and $\int_{-\infty}^{\infty} f(x) dx = 1$. It is straightforward to show that the normal curve (2.8) satisfies these properties. For example, if X is a random variable which follows a normal distribution with known mean and variance, then we can calculate the probability that X lies between any two real numbers by a process of integration using equation (2.8). Note that the PDF of the normal distribution is a function of only two parameters the mean μ and the variance σ^2.

A useful transformation associated with normal distribution is that any arbitrary normal distribution can be transformed to a *standard normal distribution* with mean zero and variance 1. This is achieved by subtracting the mean from the random variable and dividing by the standard deviation (or square root of the variance). This transformation is illustrated in the following expression:

$$X \sim N(\mu, \sigma^2) \Rightarrow Z = \frac{X - \mu}{\sigma} \sim N(0,1) \qquad (2.10)$$

Transformation to the standard normal distribution is useful because integrals of the standard normal or Z function have been tabulated and are available either in books of statistical tables or in many statistics and econometric textbooks. This allows statisticians to calculate either critical values or confidence intervals for any arbitrary normal distribution.

The integral of the normal PDF gives the probability that the random variable X lies between the limits of integration.

In the example below, the probability that X is greater than 1.645 is given by the shaded area. This is equal to 5% of the total area under the curve.

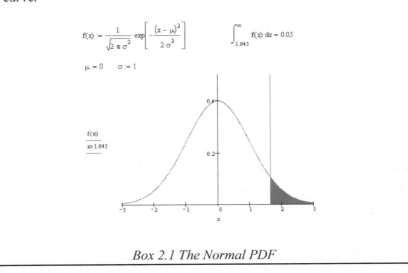

Box 2.1 The Normal PDF

Another useful feature of the normal distribution is that linear combinations of normally distributed random variables will themselves follow a normal distribution. For example, let $X_1 \sim N\left(\mu_1, \sigma_1^2\right)$ and $X_2 \sim N\left(\mu_2, \sigma_2^2\right)$ be independent normal random variables. If a and b are constants then a linear combination of the variables using a and b as weights has the following normal distribution:

$$aX_1 + bX_2 \sim N\left(a\mu_1 + b\mu_2, a^2\sigma_1^2 + b^2\sigma_2^2\right) \tag{2.11}$$

The normal distribution is unique in having this property and therefore, if we can assume normality, this is very useful in deriving the distribution of random variables which are functions of other random variables. Of course, the fact that the normal distribution has convenient properties is not a reason in itself to assume normality but, as we saw earlier in our discussion of the central limit theorem, there are often good reasons to assume that random variables are approximately normally distributed in large enough samples.

2.5 The Probability Density Function and the Moments of the Distribution

The *moments* of a distribution are the expectations of integer powers of the random variable in question. For example, if X is a random variable, then its first three moments are $E(X), E(X^2)$ and $E(X^3)$. These are the *raw moments* of the distribution. Apart from the first moment, it is usually more convenient to work in terms of the *central moments* which are the expectations of the deviation of the random variable from its mean (or first moment). Thus the second central moment of the random variable X can be written as $E(X - E(X))^2 = \sigma^2$ which is the variance of X. Higher order moments are often scaled by the standard deviation to obtain measures such as *skewness* $= E(X - E(X))^3 / \sigma^3$ and *kurtosis* $= E(X - E(X))^4 / \sigma^4$. These measures are useful in characterising the shape of a distribution and are often referred to as the moments of the distribution even though, strictly speaking, they are transformations of the raw moments. We will adopt this convention in the rest of this chapter

If we know the PDF of a distribution then we can write the moments in terms of this function. For example, the mean of the distribution can be written:

$$\mu = E(X) = \int_a^b x f(x) dx \tag{2.12}$$

By integrating $x f(x)$ over the range of possible values for X (where b is the maximum possible value of X and a is the minimum possible value) we are effectively taking a weighted average of these possible values with the weights being the probabilities $X = x$ is observed. Similarly, the variance of X can be written:

$$\sigma^2 = E(X - E(X))^2 = \int_a^b (x - \mu)^2 f(x) dx \tag{2.13}$$

Higher order moments can then be calculated by integrating a function of the form $\int_a^b (x - E(x))^k f(x) dx$ and then scaling by σ^k.

We have already seen that, in the case of the normal distribution, the first two moments fully characterise the shape of the PDF and are therefore the only parameters we need to know. This can be seen by the fact that the equation (2.8) has only two parameters μ and σ^2. This is not the case for other distributions where higher order moments become important. In particular, the third and fourth moments become important because they capture features such as skewness and kurtosis of the distribution.

2.6 Other Useful Distributions

Although the normal distribution is extremely important, there are a number of other distributions which are useful for econometrics. In particular, the *chi-Squared*, *F* and *student's t* distributions will all figure prominently in our discussion of econometric practice. We will consider each in turn and discuss the nature of the distribution, the sorts of data which might be characterised by such a distribution and what the theory tells us about the moments of each distribution.

Let us first consider the chi-squared distribution. Suppose we have k independent random variables $Z_j : j = 1, \ldots, k$ each of which follows a normal distribution with mean 0 and variance 1. This is not unduly restrictive because we have already seen that any normal distribution can be written in this form with an appropriate transformation. Now let us define the following random variable:

$$X = \sum_{j=1}^{k} Z_j^2 \qquad (2.14)$$

The random variable defined by (2.14) is said to follow a *chi-squared distribution with k degrees of freedom*. Variables with a chi-squared distribution arise naturally when we consider statistics which are defined as the sum of squared variables e.g. the residual sum of squares for a regression equation. Critical values for the chi-squared distribution with different degrees of freedom are given in most standard books of statistical tables.

For values of k greater than 2, the chi-squared distribution has the characteristic shape shown in Box 2.2. The value of the PDF is zero at $x = 0$, it then increases to a peak value for some positive value of x and then declines asymptotically to zero as x becomes large. The distribution exhibits *positive* or *right skew* in that the right tail of the distribution is longer than the left tail. This means that more of the mass (or area) of the distribution is concentrated on the left rather than the right of the PDF and contrasts with the normal distribution which is symmetric i.e. the mass of the distribution is evenly divided between the left and right tails for the normal. This characteristic shape is only observed for $k > 2$. If $k = 1$ or 2 then it is no longer the case that the chi-squared distribution has a PDF which takes the value 0 at $x = 0$. Instead, the value of the PDF tends to infinity as x tends to zero.

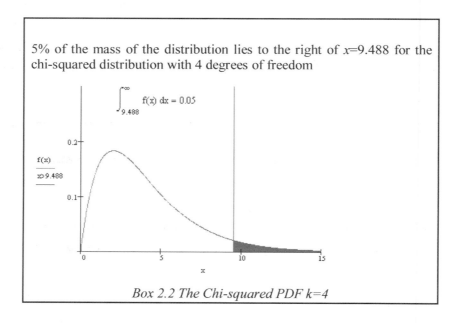

Box 2.2 The Chi-squared PDF k=4

Although it is beyond the scope of this book, it is fairly straightforward to show that the mean and the variance of a random variable which follows a chi-squared distribution with k degrees of freedom are given by the values k and $2k$ respectively. Most books of statistical tables give tables of critical values of the chi-squared distribution for different degrees of freedom. Finally, we should note that as k becomes large, the asymmetry which we have observed in the PDF of the chi-squared distribution becomes less pronounced. In the limit, for large k, the chi-squared distribution will look more and more like the normal distribution (as is predicted by the central limit theorem).

The next distribution we will consider is the *F* distribution. Suppose we have two random variables each of which follows a chi-squared distribution. In particular, let us assume that $X_1 \sim \chi_m^2$ and $X_2 \sim \chi_n^2$. Now let us define the following random variable as the ratio of the two chi-squared variables each of which is divided by its degrees of freedom.

$$X = \frac{X_1/m}{X_2/n} = \frac{X_1}{X_2}\frac{n}{m} \tag{2.15}$$

The random variable *X* defined in equation (2.15) follows an *F distribution with m and n degrees of freedom*. This is written as $X \sim F_{m,n}$. The F-distribution arises naturally in econometric analysis when we consider the ratios of variables which are constructed as the sum of squared random variables. As we will see in later chapters this situation arises frequently when we perform tests of restrictions in linear regression models.

For *m>4* the *F* distribution has a similar shape to the *chi-squared* distribution.

The graph to the right shows the *F* distribution with *m=10* and *n=10*. In this case 5% of the mass of the distribution lies to the right of *x = 2.978*.

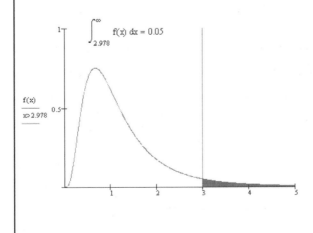

Box 2.3 The F-distribution PDF m=n=10

F distributions with m less than 4 do not have the typical shape illustrated in Box 2.3. For $m=3$ $f(0)>0$, while for $x=1$ or 2, $f(x)\to\infty$ as $x\to0$, rather like we saw for the chi-squared distribution. Another similarity with the chi-squared distribution is that as *both m and n* become large, the shape of the F distribution becomes symmetric.

Another distribution which will prove useful is the *student's t distribution*. Suppose X_1 is a random variable that follows a standard normal distribution i.e. $X_1 \sim N(0,1)$ and X_2 is a random variable that follows a chi-squared distribution with k degrees of freedom i.e. $X_2 \sim \chi^2_k$. It can be shown that the random variable defined in equation (2.16) follows a *student's t distribution* with k degrees of freedom.

$$X \sim \frac{X_1}{\sqrt{X_2 / k}} \tag{2.16}$$

Student's t distribution is often referred to simply as the t distribution. It arises in econometrics (and in many other statistical situations) when we wish to conduct hypothesis tests on a variable which we assume is normally distributed but for which we do not know the variance. We will see in subsequent chapters that tests for the significance of regression coefficients fall into this category.

The shape of the PDF of the t distribution looks very much like that of the standard normal distribution. It is symmetric around zero and has the characteristic 'bell shape' of the normal distribution. However, the t-distribution has 'fatter tails' than those of the normal distribution. By this we mean that more of the mass of the distribution lies in its tails than is the case of the normal. This means that 'extreme events' (or values of the random variable that lie in the tails) are more likely for the t distribution. The difference between the two distributions is illustrated in the diagram given in Box 2.4

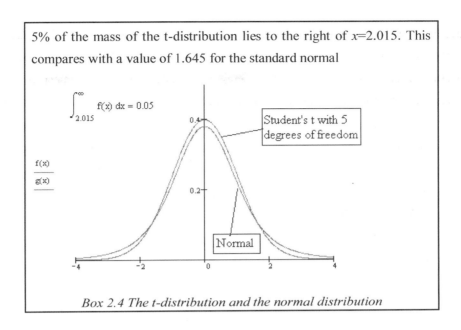

5% of the mass of the t-distribution lies to the right of $x=2.015$. This compares with a value of 1.645 for the standard normal

Box 2.4 The t-distribution and the normal distribution

The *t*-distribution is most useful when constructing tests based on small samples. As the sample size gets larger the differences between the *t* distribution and the normal get smaller. In the limit, as the sample size becomes arbitrarily large, the *t* distribution converges on the normal. In practice, for sample sizes more than 30, it is very difficult to tell these two distributions apart.

2.7 Classical and Bayesian Statistics

The discussion of probability and statistical distributions in this chapter has implicitly made the assumption that we can repeat the experiment generating the data however many times we like. For example, in generating the probability of drawing a club from a pack of cards, it assumed we can repeat this experiment a large enough number of times for the measured frequency to converge to the true underlying probability. This makes sense for simple examples like this but becomes more difficult in more complex situations where experiments are not possible. For example, suppose we are asked to state the probability that the economy will emerge from recession during the coming year. In circumstances like this we do not have the luxury of rerunning history an arbitrary number of times to measure relative frequency.

If it is not possible to repeat experiments then the interpretation of probabilities as the values to which the relative frequency of the outcomes of experiments converge becomes problematic. Some statisticians argue that it is still possible to interpret probabilities as relative frequencies which would be generated if the experiment could be repeated while recognising that in practice this is not possible. This is the standpoint taken by the *classical* or *frequentist* school. A characteristic of the classical school is that the parameters of distributions of random variables are treated as *objective*. That is, they are fixed numbers which exist independently of the experiment being conducted or the person conducting the experiment. In contrast, the *Bayesian* school of statisticians argues that the inability to repeat experiments until the relative frequency of experiments converge means that it is not possible to treat probabilities or parameters as objective. Instead they begin with the premise that these parameters are inherently *subjective*. This means that they reflect the beliefs of the investigator rather than something external. In many economic examples the Bayesian interpretation of probabilities and distributions makes more sense than the Classical interpretation. This is because economic situations are often non-repeatable in nature. Despite this, the statistical foundations of econometrics remain firmly rooted in the Classical approach and we shall continue with this interpretation, drawing attention where possible, to situations where this can be misleading.

2.8 Summary

This chapter has been concerned with the statistical foundations necessary for an understanding of econometrics. We begin with the idea of probability and the probability distribution function of a discrete random variable. This is illustrated by the binomial distribution which gives the probability of x successes in a set of n Bernoulli trials. If the number of trials is large then we show that the binomial distribution can be approximated by a particular function (2.8) which can also be interpreted as the probability density function of the normal distribution. The normal distribution is important because the central limit theorem shows that if we take the mean of a large number of independent random variables then this will follow a normal distribution. It is also important because it provides the basis for the development of a number of other distributions which are useful for the econometrician including the chi-squared, F and student's t distributions.

Exercises for Chapter 2

Exercise 1

The following table gives population data for the UK in 2007 taken from the ONS database. The data are broken down into categories of employment and by gender.

	Male	Female
Employed	12950	12254
Self-employed	2762	1054
Unemployed	944	709
Not economically active	13260	17042
Total	29916	31059

UK Population in 2007 (thousands) taken from ONS database

(a)   Create a new table which contains the joint probabilities of an individual worker falling into each of the different categories.

(b)   Calculate the marginal probabilities for the rows and columns and check that these add up to one (there may be a slight rounding error).

(c)   Calculate the conditional probability that an individual is male given that they are self-employed and compare this with the marginal probability that they are female given that they are self-employed. How would you interpret your answer?

(d)   Calculate the conditional probability that an individual is unemployed given that they are male and compare this with the marginal probability that they are unemployed given that they are female. How would you interpret your answer?

Exercise 2

The uniform distribution for a continuous random variable X has PDF $f(x)=1/(b-a)$ where b and a are the maximum and minimum values of X. Using the moments approach (equations (2.12) and (2.13)) show that the mean and the variance of X are given by the following expressions.

$$\mu = \frac{a+b}{2}$$

$$\sigma^2 = \frac{(b-a)^2}{12}$$

Exercise 3

X and Y are independent normal random variables with distribution $X \sim N(\mu_X, \sigma_X^2)$ and $Y \sim N(\mu_Y, \sigma_Y^2)$. Calculate the distributions of $X+Y$ and $X-Y$ respectively.

Chapter 3: Statistical Inference

3.1 Statistics and Inference

Classical statistical theory begins with the idea that the random variables which are of interest to us are generated by a distribution which is unknown but about which we can draw inferences based on observation. Before we can begin our discussion we need to define some terms. First of all, suppose we have a set of N independent random variables each of which has PDF $f(x)$. Because the variables are independent we can therefore write the joint PDF as $f(x_1)f(x_2)...f(x_N)$. A set of random variables of this type is referred to as a *random sample*. Next, we can define a *statistic* as a function of one or more random variables which does not depend on any unknown parameters.

For example, given a random sample $X_1, X_2, ..., X_n$ we can write the sample mean as:

$$\bar{X} = \frac{1}{N}\sum_{i=1}^{N}X_i \tag{3.1}$$

This satisfies the condition for a statistic because it does not depend on any unknown population parameters. Similarly, the sample variance is written:

$$\hat{\sigma}^2 = \frac{1}{N-1}\sum_{i=1}^{N}\left(X_i - \bar{X}\right)^2 \tag{3.2}$$

and again, this qualifies as a statistic because it does not depend on any unknown parameters. Note however, that in both cases the distribution of these statistics will depend on the unknown parameters which describe the distribution of the random variables X_i.

Let us assume that the random variable X_i follows a normal distribution. A common objective of statistical analysis is to use the sample data to estimate the unknown population parameters μ and σ^2 and, moreover, to use these estimates to make *inferences* about the parameters. The main practical problems for the econometrician arise because of the nature of the data we are forced to work with. In most cases these data do not match the definition of a random sample and, as such, the statistics we estimate do not have the distributions derived under the ideal assumptions of statistical theory. The role of econometrics as a discipline is to analyse the implications of imperfect data of this type and to suggest methods for dealing with the problems it generates.

3.2 Sampling

A random sample means that there is an equal probability of selecting any member of the population as part of the sample to be examined. This is often motivated by stylised examples such as the drawing of different coloured balls from an urn. Suppose we have an urn containing both black balls and white balls and we wish to draw a random sample to test the hypothesis that there is an equal number of each colour in the urn. For a controlled experiment of this type it is easy to construct a random sample. We simply make sure the experimenter cannot see the colour of the balls prior to making the draw.

In more complex situations it may be more difficult to ensure a random sample. For example, suppose we wish to take a random sample of households to investigate expenditure on a particular consumer product. We might dial random telephone numbers from the directory and interview the person answering. Although this sounds like a reasonable procedure it is anything but random. First, this procedure automatically eliminates from the sample all those households which do not have a listed number. This may be because they do not have a telephone or because they choose not to be listed. In either case a group of households who are likely to have somewhat different characteristics from the rest of the population are excluded. Second, only those calls which are actually answered will be considered. This will bias the sample according to the time of day at which the calls are made. If the calls were made during working hours then the sample will tend to over-represent households in which there is at least one member who is not currently employed. In general, sampling procedures which look random may be subject to subtle forms of sample selection bias when we think about them more carefully.

Since it is often very difficult to obtain a truly random sample, statisticians often use a system of *stratified sampling* to obtain a sample which is genuinely representative of the population as a whole. Usually this will involve sampling different sub-groups in numbers which reflect their share in the overall population. For example, we might divide the sample up into different age-bands and ensure that the numbers we interview in each reflects the proportions that they make up of the total population. This is the process used in the design of large studies such as the Family Expenditure Survey, which monitors expenditure on goods and services by different types of household. Although procedures like this may look non-random, they are nevertheless more likely to produce samples which approximate a genuinely random sample than less structured approaches.

One way of thinking of the sampling problem is to think of each observation as an experiment. To be a genuine experiment, the results must be independent of the experiments that have gone before. When using cross-section data this seems a reasonable analogy. We can think of the process of generating a new observation as akin to conducting a new experiment and enlarging the sample. However, when dealing with time-series data the analogy begins to break down. In what sense does a new time-series observation constitute an independent observation? The answer is that in many cases it does not. For example, when new GDP estimates are reported each quarter, the figures released do not constitute a random drawing from the population of possible outcomes. Instead, they depend heavily on the recent history of the economy and, in particular, on the behaviour of GDP over the recent past. To justify the use of classical statistical methods with time-series data we necessarily have to make strong assumptions about the distribution of the variables in questions. In particular, we need to make the assumption that the series in question is *stationary* or that its moments are independent of time. We will discuss this issue in greater detail in subsequent chapters but, for the moment, we will simply assume that the necessary conditions hold and that we can treat time-series data in the same way as we treat experimental or survey data.

Taking all these considerations into account, and assuming that we can generate a true random sample, then we can define the *sampling distribution* as the probability distribution of a statistic based on a random sample of size N. Note that the sampling distribution does not refer to a particular sample of data. Instead it is the distribution of all possible samples of a given size. The sampling distribution is determined by the underlying distribution of the population generating each observation, the statistic concerned and the sample size. The sampling distribution of a statistic is distinct from its *asymptotic distribution* which is the limit of the sampling distribution as the sample size becomes large i.e. as $N \to \infty$.

3.3 Hypothesis Testing

The process of using a sample of data to draw inferences about population parameters leads naturally to the topic of *hypothesis testing*. A hypothesis test requires the following three essential elements:

1. A hypothesis to be tested (usually described as the *null hypothesis*) and another hypothesis against which it will be examined (the *alternative hypothesis*).
2. A *test statistic* whose distribution is known under the assumption that the null hypothesis is true.
3. A *decision rule* which determines the circumstances under which the null hypothesis will be rejected.

The first of these elements is normally determined by economic theory. However, the second two elements depend more on statistical theory. The test statistic we use will depend on the assumptions we make about the statistical distribution of the variables we examine while the decision rule will depend on the costs of making either Type I or Type II errors. A Type I error is the case where we reject the null hypothesis when it is true, while a Type II error is the case where we fail to reject the null hypothesis when it is false.

Usually the decision rule involves fixing the *size* of the test, or the probability that we make a Type I error. The size of the test gives the proportion of experiments which would be expected to incorrectly reject the null hypothesis, i.e. to generate a *false positive* result. It is usually expressed as a percentage e.g. a 5% size implies that we would be willing to accept five false positive results in every 100 experiments. Test size is usually set at a fairly low level so that we reduce the probability of a false positive result in any individual experiment. However, common test sizes such as 5% and 1% are really arbitrary choices which are often used because they are conventional rather than because of any conscious choice by the researcher. Ideally, the choice of test size should reflect the researchers view of the costs of a false positive result.

32

As an example, let us consider a situation in which we wish to use a sample of data to test a hypothesis about the population mean. For simplicity, we will assume that each observation is a random experiment in which the outcome follows a normal distribution. The first stage is to specify the hypothesis we wish to text. Suppose, for example, that we wish to test the null hypothesis $H_0 : \mu = \bar{\mu}$ against the alternative $H_1 : \mu \neq \bar{\mu}$. Using the results in Appendix 3.1 we can derive a test statistic of the form

$$\frac{\bar{X} - \bar{\mu}}{\sigma / \sqrt{N}} \sim N(0,1) \tag{3.3}$$

whose distribution is known under the null. In this case the statistic will follow a standard normal distribution.

If we knew the population variance then we could use (3.3) directly as our test statistic. Unfortunately, this is rarely the case and we must substitute an estimate for σ in (3.3) in order to construct an operational test statistic. By doing this however, we will change its distribution. Consider, for example, the effects of replacing σ by its estimate $\hat{\sigma}$. From the results in the appendix we have $(N-1)\hat{\sigma}^2 / \sigma^2 \sim \chi^2_{N-1}$. Recall that the t distribution is defined as the distribution of the random variable defined as the ratio of standard normal random variable to the square root of a chi-squared random variable divided by its degrees of freedom. Therefore if we divide the random variable $\sqrt{N}(\bar{X} - \bar{\mu})/\sigma$ by $\hat{\sigma}/\sigma$ then the result will be a random variable which follows a t distribution with N-1 degrees of freedom. This gives us a working test statistic of the form:

$$t = \frac{\bar{X} - \bar{\mu}}{\hat{\sigma} / \sqrt{N}} \sim t_{N-1} \tag{3.4}$$

Unlike the previous expression (3.3) this does not contain any unknown parameters and therefore constitutes a usable test statistic.

Next we need to determine a critical value as a basis for comparison with the test statistic. The critical value is normally chosen so that it fixes the size of the test or the probability of making a Type I error. The value chosen will depend on the nature of the alternative hypothesis. If the alternative to $H_0 : \mu = \bar{\mu}$ is $H_1 : \mu \neq \bar{\mu}$ then we have a *two-sided alternative*, that is we are equally concerned about positive and negative deviations of the estimate from the hypothesised value. However, if the alternative takes the form $H_1 : \mu > \bar{\mu}$, then we have a *one-sided alternative* in which only positive deviations are of interest.

Let us first consider the case of two-sided alternative. The decision rule will involve choosing a critical value t_{crit} such that if $|t| > t_{crit}$ we reject the null. t_{crit} is set so that $p(\text{Reject } H_0 \mid H_0 \text{ true}) = \alpha$ where α is the size of the test. This is illustrated in Figure 3.2 for a *t*-test in which we have 20 observations and a 5% significance level. We must find t_{crit} so that 95% of the mass of the distribution lies between $-t_{crit}$ and t_{crit}. Alternatively, because the distribution is symmetric, we need to find t_{crit} so that 2.5% of the area under the curve lies to the right of this value. In our case this gives a value $t_{crit} = 2.093$. Tests of this kind, using a two-sided alternative, are often referred to as *two-tailed tests* because the critical value is determined by the area under both tails of the PDF.

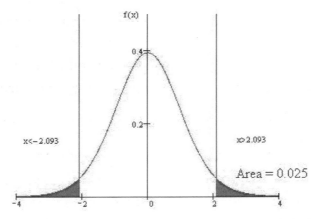

Figure 3.2. Determination of t Critical Values for a Two-Sided Alternative

Box 3.1 Finding the critical value(s)

Strictly speaking, when we have a two-tailed test, we must find a pair of critical values. For example, let Z be a statistic with a known distribution. For a test of size α, we need to find critical values such that $p\left(Z < z_c^L\right) = \alpha / 2$ and $p\left(Z > z_c^U\right) = \alpha / 2$. Taken, together these critical values give the correct size for the test because:

$$p\left(z_c^L < z < z_c^U\right) = 1 - \alpha$$

However, in the case of symmetric distributions such as Student's t or the normal we have $z_c^L = -z_c^U$ and we often therefore refer to *the* critical value on the basis that we must choose z_c such that $p\left(|z| > z_c\right) = \alpha$. Note however, that this shortcut cannot be applied for non-symmetric distributions such as the chi-squared or the F distribution. In these cases we will need to find a distinct pair of critical values if we wish to conduct two-tailed tests.

Note also that critical values are often written in such a way as to show the size of the test. For example, for a 5% critical value and a two-tailed based on the Student's t distribution, we could write the critical values as $\pm t_c^{0.025}$ or as $\pm t_c^{2.5\%}$. The superscript indicates that we need the proportion $\alpha / 2$ in both the left and right tails of the distribution to give a test of size α. For a one-tailed test, the notation is somewhat simpler because there is only one critical value which we would write as $t_c^{0.05}$ or $t_c^{5\%}$.

Consider now the case in which $H_1 : \mu > \bar{\mu}$. In this case we are only interested in cases in which the test statistic exceeds its expected value under the null. This means that the critical value is determined only by the right tail of the distribution as illustrated in Figure 3.3. The critical value in this case is given by $t_c^{0.05} = 1.729$. Tests of this kind are referred to a *one-tailed tests* for obvious reasons.

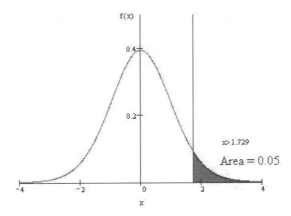

Figure 3.3. Determination of t Critical Value for a One-Sided Alternative

Example 1: Let us assume that the growth rate for the UK economy is a normally distributed random variable X with mean μ and variance σ^2. The average annual growth rate between 1949 and 2005 is calculated as $\bar{X} = 2.5495$ with standard deviation $\hat{\sigma} = 1.7662$. Can we reject the null hypothesis that $\mu = 2.0$?

To answer this question we first need to set out the null and alternative hypotheses. The form of the question implies a two-sided alternative. Therefore we will test $H_0 : \mu = 2$ against $H_1 : \mu \neq 2$. The test statistic we will use is written:

$$t = \frac{2.5495 - 2}{1.7662 / \sqrt{58}} = 2.3694$$

From the t tables we obtain a critical value(s) of ± 2.003 for a t-distribution with 57 degrees if freedom. The test statistic is greater than the positive critical bound and therefore we reject the null hypothesis in this case.

In many situations we do not want to test a null hypothesis which specifies a particular value for the unknown parameter. We may simply be interested in testing whether a parameter is greater or less than some particular value. In these cases it is more natural to use a one-sided alternative and a one-tailed test. For example, we might wish to test $H_0 : \mu \leq \bar{\mu}$, in which case it is natural to specify the alternative hypothesis as $H_1 : \mu > \bar{\mu}$. An example of this kind of test is given in Example 2.

Example 2: Let us assume that the growth rate of the Canadian economy is a normally distributed random variable X with mean μ and variance σ^2. The average annual growth rate between 1949 and 2008 is calculated as $\bar{X} = 3.9723$ with standard deviation $\hat{\sigma} = 2.5228$. Should we reject the null hypothesis that $\mu \leq 3.5$ against the alternative that it is greater than 3.5?

In this case the wording of the question indicates a one-sided alternative. The test statistic can be written:

$$t = \frac{3.9723 - 3.5}{2.5228 / \sqrt{58}} = 1.4258$$

The critical value for a one-sided alternative is 1.671 for a t-distribution with 57 degrees of freedom. Therefore in this case we cannot reject the null hypothesis in favour of the alternative at the 5% level.

3.4 Confidence Intervals

Hypothesis testing is a useful tool but sometimes leads to too much of a black and white approach to statistical inference. We are only allowed two possible choices in a hypothesis test – either we accept the null hypothesis or we reject it. In many cases a more interesting (indeed a more honest!) approach is to express our results to indicate our degree of uncertainty about the parameter in question. One approach of this kind is to give a *confidence interval*. This consists of an upper or lower bound for the parameter in question which define a $100(1-\alpha)\%$ degree of confidence about the value of the unknown parameter. This can be interpreted as stating that there is a $100(1-\alpha)\%$ chance that the range quoted contains the true unknown value of the parameter in question. Note that again the number α fixes the probability of making a Type 1 error in that it determines the chance that the range quoted does not contain the true value of the parameter.

When we define the confidence interval, it is important to note that it is the confidence interval itself which is treated as a random variable. It is common to hear loose statements of the form "there is a 95% probability that the population mean lies between these limits".

However, this is not a valid statement within classical statistical theory. In the classical framework, the population parameter μ is not a random number and therefore we cannot make probabilistic statements about it. A more accurate, though not so intuitive, statement would be to say that if the experiment used to generate the sample mean and variance was to be carried out 100 times, then 95 of the confidence intervals we would generate would be expected to contain the population mean. Thus the probabilistic statement we make refers to the interval itself not to the population parameter. Note that the Bayesian statistician would have no such qualms about making probabilistic statements about the population mean. This is because, within the Bayesian framework, there is no assumption that population parameters are fixed numbers which are independent of the investigator. Instead it is assumed that they are subjective parameters which reflect the investigator's beliefs. It is therefore perfectly valid within a Bayesian framework to refer to 'probability intervals' (or more usually 'credible intervals') rather than confidence intervals. While it would certainly be interesting to discuss this further, most econometrics uses the classical framework as its statistical foundations and we will adopt the classical terminology throughout this book.

To illustrate the determination of a confidence interval, first of all note that, for any statistical distribution, we can find lower and upper bounds $L_c^{\alpha/2}$ and $U_c^{\alpha/2}$ which define a $100(1-\alpha)\%$ confidence interval. This is particularly easy for symmetric distributions centred on zero (such as the standard normal or t-distribution) where the lower bound is equal to minus one multiplied by the upper bound. However, it is also possible for distributions such as the chi-squared or F distribution which do not satisfy these properties. For simplicity let us consider the case of generating a confidence interval for a population mean under the assumption that our data is generated by a normal distribution of the form $X_i \sim N(\mu, \sigma^2)$; $i = 1, \ldots, N$. We can show that $(\bar{X} - \mu)/\hat{\sigma} \sim t_{N-1}$ where $\bar{X}$ and $\hat{\sigma}$ are the usual estimates of the mean and standard deviation. Let $t_{N-1}^{0.025}$ be that number such that 2.5% of the mass of the t distribution with N-1 degrees of the freedom lies to the right of this value (it immediately follows that 2.5% of the mass of the distribution lies to the left of $-t_{N-1}^{0.025}$). From the results in the previous section we can therefore write:

$$p\left(-t_{N-1}^{0.025} < \frac{\bar{X} - \mu}{\hat{\sigma}} < t_{N-1}^{0.025}\right) = 0.95 \tag{3.5}$$

We can transform the inequality on the right and write this as:

$$p\left(\bar{X} - t_{N-1}^{0.025}\hat{\sigma} < \mu < \bar{X} + t_{N-1}^{0.025}\hat{\sigma}\right) = 0.95 \tag{3.6}$$

The pair of numbers $\left\{L_c^{0.025} = \bar{X} - t_{N-1}^{0.025}\hat{\sigma}, \ U_c^{0.025} = \bar{X} + t_{N-1}^{0.025}\hat{\sigma}\right\}$ give the 95% confidence interval for the unknown population mean.

Example 3 : A Confidence Interval for the Standard Deviation

We have already seen that, based on a random sample of data $X_1, X_2, ..., X_N$ where $X_i \sim N(\mu, \sigma^2)$, we have $(N-1)\hat{\sigma}^2 / \sigma^2 \sim \chi_{N-1}^2$. It is straightforward to determine lower and upper bounds for the chi-squared distribution such that:

$$p\left(L_c^{\alpha/2} < (N-1)\frac{\hat{\sigma}^2}{\sigma^2} < U_c^{\alpha/2}\right) = \alpha \tag{3.7}$$

From this we obtain:

$$p\left(\frac{N-1}{L_c^{\alpha/2}}\hat{\sigma}^2 > \sigma^2 > \frac{N-1}{U_c^{\alpha/2}}\right) = \alpha \tag{3.8}$$

which gives the $100(1-\alpha)\%$ confidence interval for the population variance.

For example, we saw in an earlier example that the sample standard deviation for UK GDP growth based on 58 annual observations from 1949 to 2007 was 1.7662. From the chi-squared tables we have $L_c^{0.025} = 38.0267$ and $U_c^{0.025} = 79.7522$. Therefore the lower and upper confidence limits for the population variance can be calculated as:

$$\frac{57}{79.7522} \times 1.7662^2 = 2.2295 \quad \text{and} \quad \frac{57}{38.0267} \times 1.7662^2 = 4.6759$$

Taking square roots yields 95% confidence limits for the standard deviation of 1.4931 and 2.1623.

Box 3.2 To Accept or to Fail to Reject ?– That is the Question

Language matters when it comes to describing the decisions we take about the null and alternative hypotheses. When we fail to reject the null, does this mean that we implicitly 'accept' it? Strictly speaking the answer is no. Failure to reject the null means precisely that – there is no implication that the null is accepted, simply that there is not enough evidence to reject it. Many statisticians get very annoyed about the misuse of language involved in describing a failure to reject as acceptance. (However, many others frequently use the term acceptance without thinking). As far as possible we will try to stick with the convention of not describing a null hypothesis as being accepted when it cannot be rejected, even if this can lead to some awkward circumlocutions at times.

3.5 P-Values

We noted earlier that one of the drawbacks of classical hypothesis testing is the 'all or nothing' nature of the decision. Consider a random variable which follows a standard normal distribution under the null hypothesis. The 5% critical values for a two-tailed test are ± 1.96. Therefore, using a 5% significance level, we would fail to reject the null if the test statistic was 1.95 but reject if it was 1.97. Any reasonable investigator would however, realise that there was virtually no difference between these two cases.

An alternative approach to statistical inference is to make use of *p-values* to assess express our degree of confidence in our results. The p-value is a function of the test statistic. What it involves is evaluating the cumulative density function for the observed value of the test statistic. Instead of deciding on a critical value and then basing an accept/reject decision on this one value, the p-value approach asks the question at what level of significance would our test statistic lead us to reject the null?

Figure 3.3 illustrates the determination of the P-value for a test statistic of 1 and a standard normal distribution. The function $F(x)$ is the cumulative normal density function. If the test statistic is equal to 1 then $F(1) = 0.8413$. This tells us that the probability of a standard normal random variable taking a value of 1 or less is equal to 0.8413. Alternatively, $1 - F(1) = 0.1587$ gives us the significance level at which we would reject the null hypothesis that the random variable has a mean of zero on the basis of a one-tailed test. Thus the p-value gives us a more flexible way of assessing a test statistic. Rather than allowing only an accept/reject decision it allows us to assess the strength of the evidence for rejection of the null hypothesis.

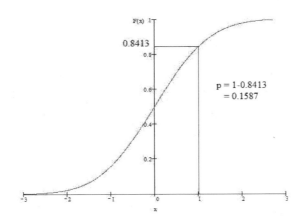

Figure 3.3: Determination of the p-value

Let us consider another example of a case in which the p-value might prove useful. Suppose we have two random samples of data $X_1, X_2, ..., X_{N_1}$ and $Y_1, Y_2, ..., Y_{N_2}$. In each case we assume that the observations are generated as independent drawings from normal distributions of the form $X_i \sim N(\mu_X, \sigma_X^2)$ and $Y_i \sim N(\mu_Y, \sigma_Y^2)$. Now suppose we wish to test the null hypothesis that the population variances are the same i.e. $H_0 : \sigma_X^2 = \sigma_Y^2 = \sigma^2$. From results we have already established we have $(N_1 - 1)\hat{\sigma}_X^2 / \sigma^2 \sim \chi_{N_1 - 1}^2$ and $(N_2 - 1)\hat{\sigma}_Y^2 / \sigma^2 \sim \chi_{N_2 - 1}^2$ under the null hypothesis. Therefore, dividing each of these expressions by the degrees of freedom and taking the ratio will give us a random variable which follows an F distribution. i.e.

$$\frac{\hat{\sigma}_X^2}{\hat{\sigma}_Y^2} \sim F_{N_1 - 1, N_2 - 1} \tag{3.9}$$

The p-value for this test statistic gives us the probability that we will make a Type I error if we reject the null hypothesis.

Example 4: Annual data for UK GDP growth between 1949 and 2007 gives an estimate of the standard deviation equal to 1.7662 while US data for 1949 to 2008 gives an estimate of 2.3472. Now suppose we wish to test the hypothesis that growth is equally as variable for the two economies. A test statistic can be calculated as:

$$\left(\frac{2.3721}{1.7662}\right)^2 = 1.8038 \tag{3.10}$$

Under the null hypothesis this is distributed as F with 58 and 57 degrees of freedom. The F-tables do not give enough fine detail to determine the p-value in this case but we can easily determine it using the statistics utility provided with this book. The value we obtain is 1-0.9864= 0.0136 which indicates that, while we would reject the null hypothesis that the variances are equal at the 5% level, we would not reject at the 1% level.

3.6 Higher Order Moments

One of the advantages of the normal distribution is that we only need to know its first two moments (the mean and the variance) in order to know everything about it. When we consider other distributions we need to consider higher order moments such as *skewness* and *kurtosis*. Skewness measures the extent to which the mass of the distribution (the area under the PDF) is unevenly distributed to the left and right of the mean. Kurtosis is a measure of the 'peakedness' of the distribution i.e. the frequency of extreme deviations from the mean – usually measured relative to the normal distribution.

The skewness of a random variable X is defined as:

$$\gamma_1 = E\left[\left(\frac{X - \mu}{\sigma}\right)^3\right] \tag{3.11}$$

This is normally estimated using the formula given in equation (3.12) even though this will be biased in small samples. However, as the sample size gets larger, this will converge on the true value.

$$\hat{\gamma}_1 = \frac{1}{N} \sum_{i=1}^{N} \left(\frac{X_i - \bar{X}}{\hat{\sigma}} \right)^3 \qquad (3.12)$$

The skewness coefficient measures the degree of asymmetry of the sampling distribution in that it measures the extent to which the mass of the distribution lies to the right or the left of the sample mean. For a normally distributed variable we would expect to observe a skewness coefficient close to zero. This is because observations should be evenly distributed around the mean and, because we are raising deviations to an odd power in (3.12), the effects of positive and negative deviations should approximately cancel out. If $\hat{\gamma}_1 > 0$ then this indicates positive (or right) skew in the PDF and the mass of the distribution is concentrated to the left. An example of this is the chi-squared distribution with degrees of freedom greater than two.

Kurtosis is based on the fourth moment of the distribution. The theoretical kurtosis coefficient is defined as:

$$\gamma_2 = E\left[\left(\frac{X - \mu}{\sigma} \right)^4 \right] \qquad (3.13)$$

For the normal distribution, we have $\gamma_2 = 3$. Because we are often interested in comparing distributions with the normal, kurtosis is sometimes expressed as $\gamma_3 - 3$ or *excess kurtosis*. The kurtosis coefficient can be estimated using the formula given in equation (3.14). Again, this will be biased in small samples, but the bias will go to zero as the sample size gets larger.

$$\hat{\gamma}_2 = \frac{1}{N} \sum_{i=1}^{N} \left(\frac{X_i - \bar{X}}{\hat{\sigma}} \right)^4 \qquad (3.14)$$

If kurtosis is less than 3 then the distribution is said to be *platykurtic* or 'flatter' than the normal distribution. An extreme example of a platykurtic distribution is the uniform distribution which is effectively perfectly flat. In contrast, if kurtosis is greater than 3 then the distribution is said to be *leptokurtic* or 'more peaked' than the normal distribution. In cases like this, more of the mass of the distribution will be found in the tails than is the case for the normal distribution. A good example of a leptokurtic distribution is the *t* distribution with a fairly small number of degrees of freedom. Examples of platykurtic and leptokurtic distributions are given in Figure 3.1. In each case the PDF of the distribution is shown relative to that of the normal distribution.

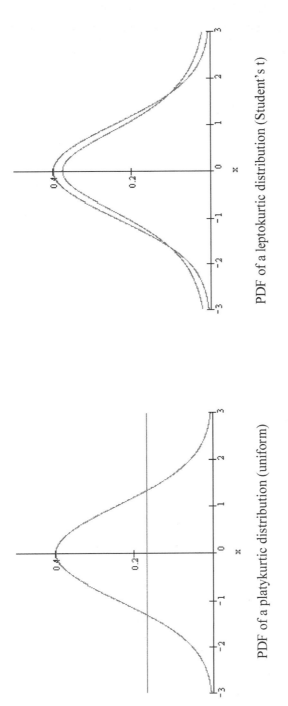

PDF of a platykurtic distribution (uniform)

PDF of a leptokurtic distribution (Student's t)

Figure 3.1. Different Forms of Kurtosis (relative to the normal distribution)

The reason why higher order moments are important is that many of our statistical testing procedures are based on the idea of a normal distribution. This is true even we consider tests based around student's t, the chi-squared or the F-distribution. In each of these cases the test statistic is ultimately based on the assumption of normality. For example, in the case of the student's t distribution we assume a normally distributed variable with unknown variance. It is the use of an estimator the sample standard deviation which means that we must use the t-distribution rather than the normal. Similarly, a chi-squared random variable is generated as the sum of squared normally distributed variables. It therefore follows that, if the underlying data are not normally distributed, it becomes extremely difficult to derive the sampling distributions of the test statistics we might want to apply. Testing for normality of a random variable is therefore an important part of the econometrician's toolkit.

In order to test whether a random variable is normally distributed we make use of the *Jarque-Bera test statistic*. This is defined in terms of the sample skewness and kurtosis coefficients as shown in equation (3.15).

$$JB = \frac{N}{6}\left[\hat{\gamma}_1^2 + \frac{1}{4}(\hat{\gamma}_2 - 3)^2 \right] \tag{3.15}$$

Under the null hypothesis that the variable in question follows a normal distribution, it can be shown that this statistic is distributed as chi-squared with two degrees of freedom. A test based on this statistic is often applied to assess if deviations from the normal distribution are severe.

Example 5: Stock market returns are often found to follow a distribution which differs significantly from the normal. For example, Table 3.1 gives sample statistics for the average return on the UK FTSE 100 index. The return is calculated as the change in the logarithm of the index from one trading day to the next. The sample period is from January 2003 to June 2008.

```
                    Sample period: 2 to 1359

      Variable                        DLOG(FTSE)

      Mean                             0.000307
      Maximum                          0.059037
      Minimum                         -0.056374
      Standard Deviation               0.009692
      Skewness                        -0.116924
      Kurtosis                         7.120151
      Jarque-Bera                    963.632841
```

Table 3.1: Returns on the UK stock market 1/1/03 to 30/5/08

Suppose we wish to test the null hypothesis that returns are normally distributed. Under the null the Jarque-Bera statistic follows a chi-squared distribution with two degrees of freedom and therefore the 5% critical value is 5.99. Given a test statistic of 963 we emphatically reject the null in favour of the alternative. From the other statistics presented in the table, we see that an important factor leading to our rejection of the null is the excess kurtosis indicated by a kurtosis coefficient of 7.12. This indicates a highly leptokurtic distribution, i.e. one in which many more observations lie in the tails of the distribution than would be expected with a normal distribution. Therefore if we had assumed a normal distribution we would considerably underestimate the probability of extreme observations in stock market returns. A fact such as this is of obvious interest to stock market traders who wish to estimate the chances of being caught out by a sudden crash in the market.

Exercises for Chapter 3

```
            Sample period: 1 to 50 (Undated Data)

            Variable                      Ratio

            Mean                       60.925342
            Maximum                   106.116351
            Minimum                    10.000000
            Standard Deviation         20.922939
            Skewness                   -0.027204
            Kurtosis                    2.394301
            Jarque-Bera                 0.770481
```

The table above gives data for the ratio of consumption to Gross Domestic Product for 50 economies.

Exercise 1

Test the null hypothesis that the population mean is greater than 55%

Exercise 2

Test the null hypothesis that the population mean is equal to 65%

Appendix 3.1 The Degrees of Freedom Correction

Note that in the expression for the variance (3.2) we divide by N-1 rather N. This is sometimes referred to as the *degrees of freedom correction*. The degrees of freedom correction can appear mysterious or arbitrary. However, it follows naturally from the construction of the estimator of sample variance. To demonstrate this, note that we can write:

$$\sum_{i=1}^{N}\left(X_i - \bar{X}\right)^2 = \sum_{i=1}^{N}\left\{\left(X_i - \mu\right) - \left(\bar{X} - \mu\right)\right\}^2$$
$$= \sum_{i=1}^{N}\left(X_i - \mu\right)^2 + \sum_{i=1}^{N}\left(\bar{X} - \mu\right)^2 - 2\sum_{i=1}^{N}\left(X_i - \mu\right)\left(\bar{X} - \mu\right)$$

In order to demonstrate the need for the degrees of freedom correction we need to find the expected value of this sum. Let us take each of its elements in turn. First, since $E\left(X_i - \mu\right)^2 = \sigma^2$, we have $E\left[\sum_{i=1}^{N}\left(X_i - \mu\right)^2\right] = N\sigma^2$. Next, by definition of the sample mean, we have $\bar{X} - \mu = 1/N\sum_{i=1}^{N}\left(X_i - \mu\right)$ and therefore:

$$E\left[\sum_{i=1}^{N}\left(\bar{X} - \mu\right)^2\right] = N \times \frac{1}{N}E\left(X_i - \mu\right)^2 = \sigma^2$$

Finally, since we have $\sum_{i=1}^{N}\left(X_i - \mu\right)\left(\bar{X} - \mu\right) = 1/N\sum_{i=1}^{N}\left(X_i - \mu\right)^2$, taking expectations yields:

$$E\left[\sum_{i=1}^{N}\left(X_i - \mu\right)\left(\bar{X} - \mu\right)\right] = \sigma^2$$

Putting these expectations together yields:

$$E\left[\sum_{i=1}^{N}\left(X_i - \bar{X}\right)^2\right] = N\sigma^2 + \sigma^2 - 2 \times \sigma^2 = \left(N - 1\right)\sigma^2 \tag{3.16}$$

Therefore, to obtain an unbiased estimator of the sample variance, we must divide by N-1 rather than N.

Note that as the sample size N increases then the bias resulting from dividing by N rather than N-1 will become arbitrarily small. To illustrate this, consider the diagram below. This shows the ratio of an unbiased estimator to the biased estimator given by the expression $f(N) = N/(N-1)$. For small samples the bias is quite large but once the sample size is greater than 30 the bias becomes negligible.

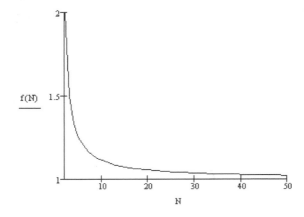

Appendix 3.2 Distribution of the Sample Mean and the Sample Variance

Suppose we have a random sample of variables $X_i : i = 1,...,N$. Each individual variable is assumed to follow a normal distribution with mean μ and variance σ^2, i.e. $X_i \sim N(\mu, \sigma^2)$. The sample mean is a linear combination of normal random variables and will therefore itself follow a normal distribution. What we need to do is to find its mean and its variance.

Consider first the mean. We have:

$$E(\bar{X}) = E\left(\frac{1}{N}\sum_{i=1}^{N} X_i\right) = \frac{1}{N} E(X_1 + X_2 + ... + X_N)$$

$$= \frac{1}{N}(E(X_1) + E(X_2) + ... + E(X_N))$$

Now by assumption $E(X_i) = \mu$ for all values of i. Therefore we have $\mu_{\bar{X}} = \mu$. This shows that the sample mean is an unbiased estimator of the unknown population mean.

The variance of the sample mean is defined as:

$$E(\bar{X} - E(\bar{X}))^2$$

we have already shown that $E(\bar{X}) = \mu$ so this can be written as:

$$E(\bar{X} - \mu)^2$$

Expanding this expression yields:

$$E(\bar{X} - \mu)^2 = E\left(\frac{1}{N}\sum_{i=1}^{N} X_i - \mu\right)^2 = \frac{1}{N^2} E\left(\sum_{i=1}^{N} X_i - N\mu\right)^2$$

$$= \frac{1}{N^2} E\left(\sum_{i=1}^{N}(X_i - \mu)^2\right)$$

$E(X_i - \mu)^2 = \sigma^2$ for all values of i and therefore:

$$\sigma_{\bar{X}}^2 = \frac{N\sigma^2}{N^2} = \frac{\sigma^2}{N}$$

Putting these results together we have established that, under our assumptions, the sample mean will follow a normal distribution with mean equal to the population mean of the distribution for the underlying random variable. The variance of the sample mean is equal to the variance of the underlying distribution divided by the number of observations i.e.

$$\bar{X} \sim N\left(\mu, \frac{\sigma^2}{N}\right)$$

One implication of this is that the variance of the sample mean will fall as the number of observations increases and in the limit will go to zero as $N \to \infty$. Using the transformation for the standard normal distribution we have:

$$\frac{\bar{X} - \mu}{\sigma / \sqrt{N}} \sim N(0,1)$$

It is a little trickier to derive the distribution of the sample variance and we will offer only an heuristic derivation here. Consider the expression $\sum_{i=1}^{N}(X_i - \bar{X})^2$, because of the definition of the sample mean, this consists of the sum of N-1 independent sums of squares, each of which has expected value σ^2. Dividing by σ^2 means that we have an expression of the form $\sum_{i=1}^{N}((X_i - \bar{X})/\sigma)^2$ which consists of the sum of N-1 squared standard normal random variables and hence has a chi-squared distribution with N-1 degrees of freedom. Now consider again the definition of the sample variance given in equation (3.2). Multiplying both sides by N-1 and dividing by σ^2 yields:

$$(N-1)\frac{\hat{\sigma}^2}{\sigma^2} = \sum_{i=1}^{N}\left(\frac{X_i - \bar{X}}{\sigma}\right)^2$$

We have established that the right-hand side of this expression has a χ^2_{N-1} distribution. Hence it follows that $(N-1)\hat{\sigma}^2 / \sigma^2 \sim \chi^2_{N-1}$. This result will prove useful in a number of derivations in the main text.

Chapter 4: The bivariate regression model

4.1 The bivariate linear regression model

Regression analysis is the most important tool which economists use to quantify their models. Economic theory provides explanations of linkages between variables of interest e.g. the relationship between consumption expenditures and disposable income. However, theory rarely gives precise values for the size of the response of one variable to another. For this we must turn to econometrics and, in particular to regression analysis. The regression model provides a mechanism by which the response of one variable to another can be quantified and evaluated from a statistical perspective. It therefore acts as one of the key items in the toolkit of the applied social scientist and the objective of this chapter is to discuss how it can be used sensibly in the investigation of economic relationships.

We will begin with a discussion of the simplest possible case - the bivariate linear regression model. This consists of a single endogenous variable Y linked to a single exogenous variable X by a linear relationship. The parameters of interest in this model are the intercept α and the slope coefficient β as shown in equation (4.1)

$$Y_i = \alpha + \beta X_i + u_i \tag{4.1}$$

where $i = 1, ..., N$ is an index of the observations available, and u_i is a random error which introduces a stochastic element into the relationship.

In practice it is very rare that the applied econometrician will be interested in a relationship as simple as (4.1). Most of the time we deal with complex relationships in which there are several right-hand side variables and where the equation of interest may be one of a system of simultaneous equations. Nevertheless, the analysis of a simple equation like this gives us the opportunity to develop an understanding of the regression model which will be of value when it comes to dealing with more complex relationships. Therefore, in this chapter, we will present a thorough review of the bivariate regression model which will cover estimation, statistical inference and prediction.

4.2 Derivation of the OLS estimator

The problem facing the econometrician is how best to use the data available $\{(X_i, Y_i); i = 1,...N\}$ to estimate the unknown parameters of equation (4.1). Ordinary least squares (OLS) provides a simple method for the generation of such estimates which, under certain assumptions, can be shown to have the desirable properties that the estimates are both biased and efficient (in the sense that they have the lowest possible variances in the class of unbiased estimators). The method of OLS is to choose parameter estimates $\hat{\alpha}$ and $\hat{\beta}$ which minimise the sum of the squared deviations of the actual values of Y_i from the fitted values $\hat{\alpha} + \hat{\beta} X_i$. In mathematical notation we can write the problem as:

$$\min_{\hat{\alpha},\hat{\beta}} RSS = \sum_{i=1}^{N} \left(Y_i - \hat{\alpha} - \hat{\beta} X_i \right)^2 \qquad (4.2)$$

This is a relatively straightforward problem in calculus since the loss function is quadratic in the variables of interest. Differentiation with respect to $\hat{\alpha}$ and $\hat{\beta}$ yields the following pair of first order conditions for a minimum.

$$\frac{\partial RSS}{\partial \hat{\alpha}} = -2 \sum_{i=1}^{N} \left(Y_i - \hat{\alpha} - \hat{\beta} X_i \right) = 0 \qquad (4.3)$$

$$\frac{\partial RSS}{\partial \hat{\beta}} = -2 \sum_{i=1}^{N} X_i \left(Y_i - \hat{\alpha} - \hat{\beta} X_i \right) = 0 \qquad (4.4)$$

Equations (4.3) and (4.4) in turn can be used to derive the following pair of simultaneous equations in $\hat{\alpha}$ and $\hat{\beta}$ which are known as *the least-squares normal equations*. Note that, since all summations here are over the full sample of data $i=1,..., N$, we have dropped the limits of the summation operator to simplify the notation:

$$\hat{\alpha} N + \hat{\beta} \sum X_i = \sum Y_i \qquad (4.5)$$

$$\hat{\alpha} \sum X_i + \hat{\beta} \sum X_i^2 = \sum X_i Y_i \qquad (4.6)$$

The solution of these equations is interesting because it demonstrates that the OLS parameter estimates are functions of the sample moments of the data. For example, dividing equation (4.5) by N immediately yields the result that the regression line passes through the sample means of the data i.e.

$$\bar{Y} = \hat{\alpha} + \hat{\beta}\bar{X} \tag{4.7}$$

Substituting $\hat{\alpha} = \bar{Y} - \hat{\beta}\bar{X}$ into (4.6) and rearranging yields:

$$\hat{\beta} = \frac{\sum X_i Y_i - \bar{Y}\sum X_i}{\sum X_i^2 - \bar{X}\sum X_i} = \frac{\sum X_i Y_i - N\bar{Y}\bar{X}}{\sum X_i^2 - N\bar{X}^2} \tag{4.8}$$

Given that $\sum X_i Y_i - N\bar{Y}\bar{X} = \sum(X_i - \bar{X})(Y_i - \bar{Y})$ and that $\sum X_i^2 - N\bar{X}^2 = \sum(X_i - \bar{X})^2$ we can write (4.8) as:

$$\hat{\beta} = \frac{\sum(X_i - \bar{X})(Y_i - \bar{Y})}{\sum(X_i - \bar{X})^2} \tag{4.9}$$

Equation (4.9) enables an intuitive interpretation of the OLS slope coefficient in terms of the sample moments of the Y and X variables. Dividing numerator and denominator by N-1 enables (4.9) to be written as $\hat{\beta} = \dfrac{\sum(X_i - \bar{X})(Y_i - \bar{Y})/(N-1)}{\sum(X_i - \bar{X})^2/(N-1)}$. The numerator of this expression is an unbiased estimator of the population covariance and the denominator is an unbiased estimator of the variance of X. Thus the slope coefficient for the bivariate regression model is equal to the ratio of the sample covariance of X and Y and the sample variance of X. We have therefore established that both the intercept and the slope coefficient estimates for the OLS model can be written in terms of the first and second sample moments of the data. Note that in our estimates of the covariance of X and Y and the variance of X, we divide by N-1 rather than by the number of observation to allow for the loss of degrees of freedom incurred when estimating sample means. In large samples this makes relatively little difference to the calculation of the sample moments and, because in this case we are taking the ratio of two sample moments, the estimate of the slope coefficient is unaffected when we use the same divisor for *both* sample moments. However, we need to be careful if we use this method to calculate the regression slope coefficient because some statistical packages and spreadsheets will use N-1 as the divisor for the variance of X and N as the divisor for the covariance of X and Y.

Example: The following data are taken from the UK Family Expenditure Survey. The Y variable is weekly expenditure on housing and the X variable is total weekly expenditure. Both variables are measured in £ sterling and are averages by income decile.

Income Decile	Weekly Expenditure on Housing	Total Weekly Expenditure
	Y	X
1	19.8	119.7
2	23.8	146.8
3	29.6	178.1
4	42.1	244.8
5	50.9	300.0
6	57.9	361.8
7	66.0	412.9
8	72.5	481.8
9	86.7	565.2
10	120.8	782.5

Table 4.1: Expenditure on housing and total expenditure by income decile

From the data in this table we can calculate the following set of sample moments:

$$\bar{Y} = 57.01 \qquad \bar{X} = 359.36$$
$$\hat{\sigma}_X^2 = 4.349 \times 10^4 \qquad \hat{\sigma}_{XY} = 6.500 \times 10^3$$

Using these sample moments we can calculate the parameters of the regression line as:

$$\hat{\beta} = \frac{6.5 \times 10^3}{4.349 \times 10^4} = 0.149 \quad \hat{\alpha} = 57.01 - 0.149 \times 359.36 = 3.465$$

and the regression line itself can be written:

$$\hat{Y}_i = 3.465 + 0.149 X_i$$

Thus our estimates indicate that if total expenditure per household were to rise by £100, about £15 of that increase would go on increased housing expenditure.

4.3 Interpreting the regression line – marginal effects and elasticities

The slope coefficient of the regression line gives us an estimate of the *marginal effect* of the variable X on the variable Y. That is, we can think of $\hat{\beta}$ as an estimate of dY/dX. In addition, the use of a linear relationship implies that this marginal effect is constant for all values if X. This is actually a very strong assumption which can be misleading if taken too literally. A more reasonable assumption is that the marginal effect is approximately constant within the range of the sample data for X. If we try to use the estimated regression model to predict the value of Y using values of X which lie a long way outside the range of the data used to estimate the model, then it is likely that the predictions will prove unreliable.

The marginal effect of X on Y is not always the most interesting statistic for the investigator. In many cases a more interesting is the *elasticity*. This measures the proportional response of Y to a given proportional change in X. The elasticity can be written in mathematical terms as $\eta = (dY/Y) \div (dX/X) = (dY/dX) \times (X/Y)$. Along a linear regression line the elasticity will change because dY/dX is constant but X/Y changes if the intercept is non-zero. It is possible to obtain an elasticity estimate for a point on the regression line. For example, we can evaluate the elasticity at the sample means of the data $\hat{\eta} = \hat{\beta} \times \bar{X}/\bar{Y}$. However, it is often useful to obtain a more direct estimate of the elasticity through a modification of the regression equation itself.

Consider an alternative specification of the regression equation which is expressed in logarithms of the variables Y and X:

$$\ln(Y_i) = \alpha + \beta \ln(X_i) + u_i \qquad (4.10)$$

This is referred to as a *log-linear regression model* for obvious reasons. We can estimate this by ordinary least squares to obtain a slope coefficient $\hat{\beta}$ which can be interpreted as an estimate of the marginal effect $d\ln Y / d\ln X$. Now the first-order differential of the logarithmic function can be written as $d\ln z = dz / z$, and for small increments the ratio of the first-order differentials of $\ln Y$ and $\ln X$ will give the derivative of $\ln Y$ with respect to $\ln X$ i.e. $d\ln Y / d\ln X = dY / dX \times X / Y$. This means that the marginal effect from a log-linear model gives the elasticity of Y with respect to X and is one of the reasons why the log-linear specification is so often used in applied econometric analysis.

Let us reconsider our regression model for housing expenditure. Estimation using a linear regression equation gave a marginal effect of 0.149. This indicates that an increase in total expenditure of £100 would be associated with an increase in housing expenditure of £14.90. Now, let us estimate an equation using the same data but a log-linear specification. The following results are obtained:

$$\ln(Y_i) = -1.54 + 0.95 \ln(X_i) + \hat{u}_i$$

The slope coefficient of this equation gives us an estimate of the elasticity of housing expenditure with respect to total expenditure $\hat{\eta} = 0.95$. This means that a 1% increase in total expenditure will be associated with a 0.95% increase in housing expenditure. Note that this is consistent with our earlier estimate of the marginal effect since, if we use the linear model to estimate the elasticity at the means of the data, we obtain $\hat{\eta} = 0.149 \times 359.36 / 57.01 = 0.94$, which is very close to our estimate from the log-linear equation.

Another advantage of the log-linear specification is that the coefficient estimates do not depend on the units of measurement of the data. For example, let us consider the relationship between consumption expenditures and disposable income. These data are plotted in Figure 4. 1 and show a clear positive relationship between the two series:

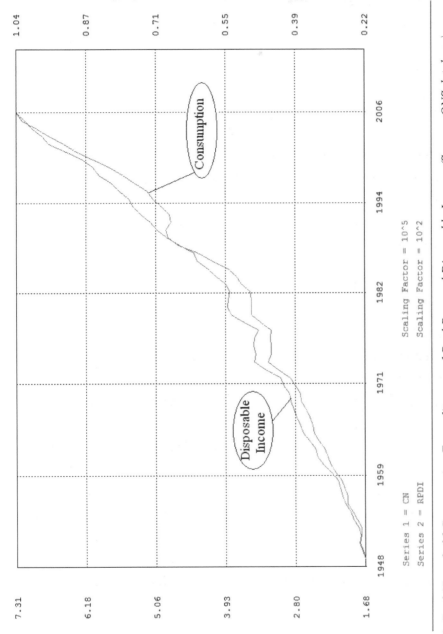

Figure 4.1: Real Household Consumption Expenditures and Real Personal Disposable Income (Source: ONS database).

As the scaling factors below Figure 4.1 indicate, the units of measurement of these series are quite different. Consumption expenditures are measured in £million at 2003 prices while the Disposable Income figures are an index with 2003 = 100. If we regress consumption on income then we obtain the following results:

$$CN_t = 4982 + 6730\,YD_t + \hat{u}_t$$

To interpret the slope coefficient in this case we need to know the units of measurement. What the slope coefficient indicates is that the marginal effect of a rise of 1% point in the index of personal disposable income will increase consumption expenditures by £6.73 bn. A result like this is clearly hard to interpret. However, if we estimate the model in log-linear form then we obtain:

$$\ln CN_t = 9.03 + 0.949\ln YD_t + \hat{u}_t$$

The slope coefficient here is considerably easier to interpret. What it indicates in this case is that a 1% rise in disposable income will increase consumption expenditures by 0.949%.

4.4. The reverse regression

In some cases the direction of causation for our economic model is obvious. However, in others it may be less so and it may be interesting to reverse the direction of causation of the regression equation. That is, instead of thinking of X as the exogenous variable and Y as the endogenous variable we might think of Y as the variable causing changes in X. An example of this might be the relationship between the stock of money and the rate of interest. Is it better to think of this in terms of the demand for money being determined by the opportunity cost of holding money balances or in terms of the rate of interest being determined by the available supply of money? Economic theory does not help here since the relationship makes sense in either direction. Indeed, the best solution might be to think of these variables as jointly determined endogenous variables rather than trying to separate them into exogenous and endogenous categories prior to estimation. However, if we are to estimate a regression equation then we must allocate one variable to the left hand side and the other to the right hand.

Consider the regression equation $Y_i = \alpha + \beta X_i + u_i$. Now it may be tempting to assume that we could estimate the marginal effect of Y on X by estimating this equation by least squares to obtain $\hat{Y}_i = \hat{\alpha} + \hat{\beta} X_i$ and then 'solving' this equation to obtain $X_i = -\hat{\alpha}/\hat{\beta} + \hat{Y}_i / \hat{\beta}$. This would yield an estimate of the marginal effect of Y on X which is equal to the reciprocal of the OLS slope coefficient from the original regression equation. Unfortunately, this procedure is quite incorrect. To see this consider the reverse regression equation $X_i = \gamma + \delta Y_i + v_i$ where γ and δ are the intercept and slope parameters and v is a random error. It is easy to see that the estimate of the slope coefficient from this regression will take the form:

$$\hat{\delta} = \frac{\sum (X_i - \bar{X})(Y_i - \bar{Y})}{\sum (Y_i - \bar{Y})^2} \tag{4.11}$$

This is clearly not equal to the reciprocal of the slope coefficient from a regression of Y on X. However, there is an interesting relationship between the least squares estimates of the slope coefficients of the original regression and the reverse regression. If we multiply these estimates together then we obtain the following result:

$$\hat{\beta} \times \hat{\delta} = \frac{\left(\sum (X_i - \bar{X})(Y_i - \bar{Y})\right)^2}{\sum (X_i - \bar{X})^2 \sum (Y_i - \bar{Y})^2} = \hat{\rho}_{XY}^2 \tag{4.12}$$

This is the square of the sample correlation coefficient of Y and X. Thus we have established a link between three measures of association between a pair of variables Y and X in that we have shown that the product of the slope coefficients from the original regression and the reverse regression is equal to the square of the correlation coefficient.

Example: An example of the differences between the regression equation and the reverse regression is given in Figure 4.2. This illustrates the relationship between a regression of inflation and monetary growth and the reverses regression for a sample of 70 economies.

Note that the sample excludes 13 economies with the highest rates of inflation from our full sample of data because their inclusion has a disproportionate effect on the estimated equations.

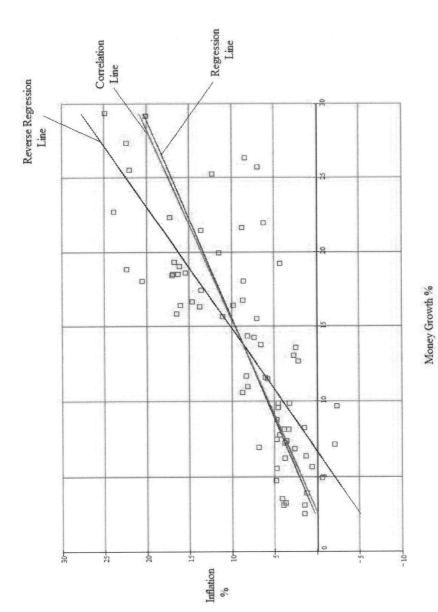

Figure 4.2. Regression lines for relationship between inflation and money growth

The basic regression line takes the form $INF_i = -1.3077 + 0.7382\ MON_i$. Now if we 'solve' this to obtain an equation for monetary growth then the resulting equation takes the form $MON_i = 1.771 + 1.3546\ INF_i$ which is quite different from the actual results from estimating the reverse regression which yields $MON_i = 6.3979 + 0.8345\ INF_i$. The reverse regression is therefore definitely not just another way of writing the original regression equation. The differences between the two can be seen clearly in Figure 4.2 in which the slopes of the two regression equations are quite different. Both equations will however pass through the sample means of the date as shown by the crossing point in the diagram. Figure 4.2 also illustrates the fact that the slopes of both the regression equations are different from the correlation. The third line in Figure 4.2 has slope equal to the sample correlation coefficient. This third line also passes through the sample means of the data to facilitate comparison with the two regression equations.

The differences between the three lines shown in Figure 4.2 are further illustrated in Box 4.1 which shows an artificial example of 10 inflation- money growth pairs: The purpose is to illustrate the difference in construction between the three lines shown in Figure 4.2. Each of these can be thought of as a 'best-fit' line in some sense but each uses a different principle in its construction. The simple regression is constructed by minimising the sum of the squared vertical distances of the scatter of points from the line. The reverse regression is constructed by minimising the sum of the squared horizontal distances and finally, the correlation line can be thought of as minimising the sum of the squared perpendicular distances of the scatter from the line. The method we choose to use to fit a line to the data will depend on our views of the causal relationships between the variables and what we wish to do with the model once it has been constructed.

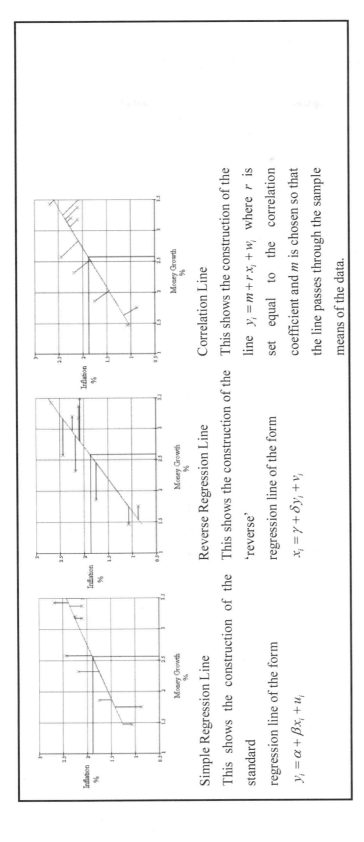

Simple Regression Line

This shows the construction of the standard regression line of the form

$$y_i = \alpha + \beta x_i + u_i$$

Reverse Regression Line

This shows the construction of the 'reverse' regression line of the form

$$x_i = \gamma + \delta y_i + v_i$$

Correlation Line

This shows the construction of the line $y_i = m + r x_i + w_i$ where r is set equal to the correlation coefficient and m is chosen so that the line passes through the sample means of the data.

Box 4.1: Alternative 'best-fit' lines

4.4 Assumptions of the classical linear regression model

So far we have concentrated on the mechanics of the regression model. However, if we wish to go further and discuss the statistical properties of the estimator, then we need to make further assumptions about the nature of the data and the properties of the random error term. There is a standard set of assumptions used as the starting point for such a discussion which we list in Table 4.2 below.

1. The error term has zero mean $E(u_i) = 0; i = 1,...N$.
2. The covariance of the error term indexed i and that indexed $j \neq i$ is zero $E(u_i u_j) = 0; i \neq j$.
3. The variance of the error term is constant $E(u_i^2) = \sigma_u^2; i = 1,...N$.
4. (a) Strong form: The X variable is non-stochastic (fixed in repeated samples).
a) (b) Weak form: The covariance of the X variable and the error is zero $E(X_i u_i) = 0$.
5. The errors follow a normal distribution.

Table 4.2: Assumptions of the Classical Linear Regression Model

Assumption 2 is described as the assumption of *serial independence*. This condition is most often a problem when we are dealing with time-series data where, for example, it might be the case that $E(u_t u_{t-1}) \neq 0$. In such circumstances we would describe the error as being serially correlated and would need to take account of this when assessing the properties of the OLS estimator. Assumption 3 is described as the assumption of *homoscedasticity*. Models which violate this condition are most often found when we are dealing with cross-section data where the size of the variance of the error term is related to the value of the exogenous variable. For example, we might have $\sigma_{u_i}^2 = \sigma^2 X_i^2$. Assumption 4 is that the X variable should be regarded as exogenous i.e. independent of any random disturbances to the relationship while assumption 5 is self-explanatory.

The assumptions listed in Table 4.2 are sometimes described as the *Gauss-Markov assumptions*. However, this is misleading. Strictly speaking, the Gauss-Markov assumptions are those needed to prove the Gauss-Markov theorem, which states that the

OLS estimator has lowest variance in the class of linear unbiased estimators. To prove this theorem we need to make assumption 1-3 plus assumption 4(a). The assumption that the errors follow a normal distribution is not necessary for the proof and therefore should not be listed as one of the Gauss-Markov assumptions. Similarly, if we replace the strong form of assumption 4 with the weaker version given in 4(b) then it is not possible to prove the Gauss-Markov theorem and hence this should not be listed as one of its assumptions.

In the discussion which follows, we will make the full set of assumptions listed in Table 4.2. We will also maintain the strong form of assumption 4, that the X variable is non-stochastic. The strong form of assumption 4 is not realistic for most econometric modelling. It assumes the ability of the investigator to replicate the input data (X values) by experimental means so that the only source of variation in the sample data is the random error term u. This is what is meant by the phrase 'fixed in repeated samples'. While such an assumption is appropriate for experimental sciences, it is clearly unrealistic for most economic applications. However, it will make it possible to derive distributional results for the OLS parameter estimates which would not be possible if we were to use the weaker form. Therefore we will maintain this assumption for the moment and consider the effects of relaxing it later.

4.4 Distribution of the OLS estimator

Consider the OLS estimator of the slope coefficient given in equation (4.9). From the original model we have $Y_i - \bar{Y} = \beta(X_i - \bar{X}) + u_i - \bar{u}$, substituting into (4.9) and noting that $\bar{u}\sum(X_i - \bar{X}) = 0$ by definition of the arithmetic mean of x, yields:

$$\hat{\beta} = \beta + \frac{\sum(X_i - \bar{X})u_i}{\sum(X_i - \bar{X})^2} \qquad (4.13)$$

Now, if we maintain the strong version of assumption 4, we can apply the expectations operator to this equation to obtain:

$$E(\hat{\beta}) = \beta + \frac{\sum (X_i - \bar{X}) E(u_i)}{\sum (X_i - \bar{X})^2} \tag{4.14}$$

Moreover, from assumption 1 we have that $E(u_i) = 0;\ i = 1, .., N$, therefore equation (4.14) yields the result that $E(\hat{\beta}) = \beta$ which states that the OLS estimator of the slope coefficient is unbiased. Note the crucial role of the strong version of assumption 4 here. Without this assumption, the expectations operator would have to apply to a complex non-linear function of the X variables and it would simply not be possibly to prove unbiasedness in this way. Instead we would have to rely on the large sample concept of consistency in which, under certain assumptions, the estimator $\hat{\beta}$ could be shown to 'converge' on the true value if the sample size is sufficiently large.

Next, consider the variance of the OLS estimator. From the results derived so far we have that $\hat{\beta} - E(\hat{\beta}) = \frac{\sum (X_i - \bar{X}) E(u_i)}{\sum (X_i - \bar{X})^2}$. Therefore, the variance of $\hat{\beta}$ is given by the following expression in equation (4.15):

$$V(\hat{\beta}) = E\left(\hat{\beta} - E(\hat{\beta})\right)^2 = E\left(\frac{\sum (X_i - \bar{X}) u_i}{\sum (X_i - \bar{X})^2} \right)^2 \tag{4.15}$$

From assumptions 2 and 3 of the CLRM we have that $E(u_i u_j) = 0; i \neq j$ and $E(u_i^2) = \sigma_u^2;\ i = 1, ..., N$. Therefore, taking expectations of the right-hand side of equation (4.15) yields:

$$V(\hat{\beta}) = \frac{\sigma_u^2}{\sum (X_i - \bar{X})^2} \tag{4.16}$$

Finally, from assumption 5 of the CLRM we have that the errors are normally distributed and from equation (4.13) we have the OLS estimator is a linear combination of the errors. Since any linear combination of normally distributed variables itself follows a normal distribution, we therefore can show that under the CLRM assumptions the OLS estimator follows a normal distribution as shown in expression (4.17):

$$\hat{\beta} \sim N\left(\beta, \frac{\sigma^2}{\sum\left(X_i - \bar{X}\right)^2}\right) \qquad (4.17)$$

Equation (4.17) illustrates an interesting feature of the regression model. Consider the denominator of the variance expression, as the sample size increases then this must also increase since the summation always involves the addition of positive numbers. Therefore, since σ_u^2 is constant, it follows that the variance of the OLS estimator tends to zero as the sample size become large i.e. the distribution of the OLS estimator is degenerate. Box 4.2 illustrates what happens to the probability density function of the OLS estimator when $\beta = 1$, $\sigma_u^2 = 1$ and $\sigma_X^2 = 1$. As the sample size increases, the variance of the OLS estimator falls reducing the spread of the probability density function. In the limit, as the sample size becomes infinite, the PDF of the OLS estimator collapses onto a vertical line going through the value β.

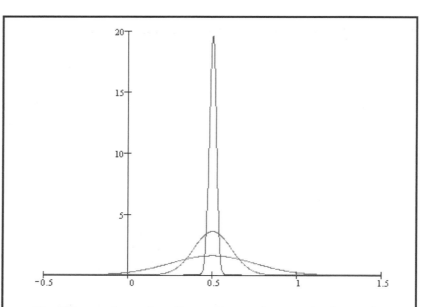

The diagram shows the effects of increasing sample size on the probability density function of the least squares slope coefficient. In all cases the distribution is centred on 0.5 but, as the sample size gets larger, the variance becomes smaller and, in the limit, the distribution collapses onto a vertical line going through the true value.

Box 4.2: Effects of the sample size on the distribution of the estimator of the regression slope

4.5 Statistical inference with the OLS estimator

The main reason why we are interested in the distribution of the OLS estimator is that we wish to use this knowledge for the purposes of statistical inference. That is we wish to be able to conduct hypothesis tests on the coefficients of the model and to construct confidence intervals for the unknown model parameters. First note that the distribution of the OLS estimator of the slope coefficient can be transformed to the standard normal distribution as shown in expression

$$\frac{\hat{\beta} - \beta}{\sigma_u / \sqrt{\sum (X_i - \bar{X})^2}} \sim N(0,1) \tag{4.18}$$

If we knew the error variance then statistical inference would be relatively simple. For example, suppose we wished to test $H_0 : \beta = \beta_0$ against $H_1 : \beta \neq \beta_0$. The test statistic for this test would be $\dfrac{(\hat{\beta} - \beta_0)}{\sigma_u / \sqrt{\sum (X_i - \bar{X})^2}}$ and we could compare this with the appropriate critical value from the standard normal tables. Similarly, we could construct $\alpha\%$ confidence intervals using the formula $\beta \pm z_c^{\alpha/2} \sigma_u / \sqrt{\sum (X_i - \bar{X})^2}$ where z is the critical value for a two-tailed test, again taken from the standard normal tables.

The problem of course is that we don't know the error variance and therefore we must use an estimate. However, once we substitute an estimated value for σ_u^2 in (4.18) then the resulting statistic no longer follows the normal distribution. Instead the test statistic can be shown to follow the Student's t distribution. As we discussed in an earlier chapter the t-distribution is in many ways similar to the normal distribution in that it is symmetric and has the characteristic 'bell-shape' of the normal distribution. Relatively more of the mass of the t-distribution lies in the tails when compared with the normal. Even this difference declines as the sample size gets larger and in large enough samples the t and normal distributions become indistinguishable.

Example: Consider the following regression equation which relates the growth rate of consumers' expenditure for the UK to the growth rate of GDP. The data are annual from 1956 to 2001. Standard errors are given in parentheses below parameter estimates.

$$\Delta c_t = \underset{(0.34)}{0.69} + \underset{(0.11)}{0.83} \, \Delta y_t + \hat{u}_t \qquad (4.19)$$

First let us consider the standard null hypothesis that the coefficients are zero against the alternative that they are non-zero. Given this alternative hypothesis, a two-tailed test is appropriate and therefore the 5% critical value for a t-test with 44 degrees of freedom is 2.01. The test statistic[2] for the intercept is $0.69/0.34 = 2.03$ while that for the slope coefficient is $0.83/0.11 = 7.54$. Therefore in both cases here we would reject the null hypothesis that the coefficients are zero in favour of the alternative that they are non-zero.

Tests of the null hypothesis that the coefficients are zero form a standard part of econometric procedure. However, this null hypothesis is not always the most interesting from the point of view of economic theory. For example, in the case of the consumption-income relationship, we might be more interested in testing the null hypothesis that the slope coefficient is equal to one against the alternative that it is less than one. This alternative hypothesis requires a one-tailed test and so the 5% critical value in this case is 1.68. The test statistic is $(0.83 - 1)/0.11 = -1.55$, therefore in this case we cannot reject the null hypothesis that the slope coefficient is equal to one.

Finally, we may be interested in presenting confidence intervals for the parameters. Suppose, for example, that we wish to calculate the 95% confidence interval for the slope coefficient. This will be given by the following expression:

$$\hat{\beta}_1 - 2.01 \times SE\left(\hat{\beta}_1\right) < \beta_1 < \hat{\beta}_1 + 2.01 \times SE\left(\hat{\beta}_1\right)$$

---

[2] The values of the test statistics here are calculated using the rounded values reported in the regression equation. Those calculated by the regression package will be slightly different since they use unrounded values. However, the difference does not change the conclusions of the testing procedure in either case.

where $\hat{\beta}_1$ is the OLS estimate of the slope coefficient and $SE\left(\hat{\beta}_1\right)$ is its standard error. Using the values reported in (4.19) this gives:

$$0.83 - 2.01 \times 0.11 < \beta_1 < 0.83 + 2.01 \times 0.11$$
$$0.61 < \beta_1 < 1.05$$

Econometricians tend to place most emphasis on the *size* of the tests they conduct rather than their *power*. The size of the test is the probability of rejecting the null hypothesis when it is true. This can always be set by the investigator through the choice of an appropriate critical value. We can think of the size of the test as the probability of generating a false positive result i.e. a Type I error. The power of a test is defined as the probability of rejecting the null hypothesis when the alternative is true. Alternatively we can think of this as one minus the probability of generating a false negative result. A false negative corresponds to a Type II error when we accept the null even though the alternative is true. Now, for a variety of reasons, it is much more difficult to determine the power of test than it is to fix its size. However, this does not mean that power is unimportant and it needs to be considered whenever we implement a particular testing procedure.

To consider the relationship between size and power, consider the case illustrated in Figure 4.3. This corresponds to a situation in which both the null and the alternative hypotheses involve specific values of an unknown parameter θ. For example we might have a test of the form $H_0 : \theta = \theta_A$ against $H_1 : \theta = \theta_B$. Figure 4.3 shows the probability density functions for H_0 when $\theta \sim N(0,1)$ and for H_1 when $\theta \sim N(3,1)$.

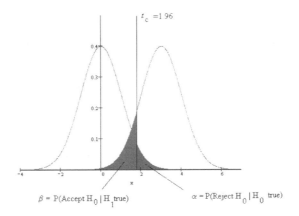

$\beta = \text{P(Accept H}_0 \mid \text{H}_1 \text{ true)}$ $\alpha = \text{P(Reject H}_0 \mid \text{H}_0 \text{ true)}$

Figure 4.3: Probability density functions for null and alternative hypotheses

The vertical line in Figure 4.3 determines the size of the test. It shows the chosen critical value for the test which determines its size. For example, in this case we have $t_c = 1.96$ which, for a standard normal distribution and a one-tailed test, indicates a significance level of 2.5%. This is illustrated by the shaded region for α which shows 2.5% of the area under the PDF for the null lying to the right of t_c. We would reject the null hypothesis at the 2.5% level if the test statistic was greater than 1.96. Next, consider the implications if the alternative hypothesis is true. The probability that we fail to reject the null is given by the area under the PDF for the alternative hypothesis to the left of the critical value. This is shown by the second shaded region in Figure 4.3 which is labelled β. The power of the test is equal to $1 - \beta$. Therefore the choice of the critical value determines both the size of the test and its power. If we increase the critical value then we lower the probability of making a Type I error but we simultaneously lower the power of the test (increase the probability of making a Type II error).

In the example given in Figure 4.3 we can write down an expression for the power of a test as $1 - \beta = 1 - \int_{-\infty}^{t_c} f\left(\hat{\theta} - \theta_B\right) d\hat{\theta}$ where f is the PDF of the random variable $\hat{\theta}$ (the estimator) and θ_B is the hypothesised value under the alternative hypothesis. Now consider the case in which we are interested in estimating the slope coefficient for a least squares regression. We know that the distribution of such an estimator is degenerate i.e. its variance falls to zero as the sample size gets large. It therefore follows that $\int_{-\infty}^{t_c} f\left(\hat{\theta} - \theta_B\right) d\hat{\theta} \to 0$ as $N \to \infty$

or the power of the test approaches one as the sample size becomes large. Another implication of this is that, for any given size of such a test, we can determine the power of the test *providing that we have enough observations*. Of course, this last point is the tricky one for econometricians who rarely have the opportunity to generate data experimentally and are forced, in general, to take the number of observations as a given. This may help us understand the lack of discussion of power in many econometrics textbooks. In an experimental science the investigator can control the power of a test by replicating the experiment an appropriate number of times. Since econometricians do not have such control the issue of power is often mentioned and then promptly ignored.

The example in Figure 4.3 indicates several other problems for the determination of the power of a statistical test. Firstly, in order to determine the probability of making a Type II error we need to assume that the alternative hypothesis takes a specific form, $H_1 : \theta = \theta_B$. In the more general cases $H_1 : \theta < \theta_B$ and $H_1 : \theta \neq \theta_B$ we cannot draw a unique PDF for the alternative hypothesis and therefore we cannot identify the power of the test with a specific number. Secondly, in order to draw the PDF of the estimator we need to know the parameters of its distribution such as the variance and possibly higher order moments. These are rarely known in advance and we must usually make use of estimates which complicate the distribution and make it harder to determine both size and power for any given test. However, the general points illustrated by the diagram and the discussion remain true for more complex cases. If we increase the size of the test, taking the number of observations as fixed, then we reduce its power. The only way to increase both the size and the power of a test simultaneously is to generate more data.

4.6 Prediction with the OLS estimator

When discussing prediction the first thing to note is that prediction and forecasting are different activities. Prediction involves the generation of a value of y given a particular value of x. For example, if we have estimated a regression equation of the form $\hat{Y}_i = \hat{\alpha} + \hat{\beta} X_i$ then the predicted value of y for $X = x_0$ is $\hat{y}_0 = \hat{\alpha} + \hat{\beta} x_0$. Forecasting generally requires us to predict values for X as well as those for Y. The main practical difference is that forecasts can be in error because we use the 'wrong' value of x whereas this is not a consideration when it comes to prediction.

We will first consider the topic of prediction. Suppose we wish to predict Y_{N+1} for a given value of $X = x_{N+1}$ having estimated the parameters of the model using data for $i = 1, ..., N$. The prediction error from the OLS estimator can be written:

$$Y_{N+1} - \hat{Y}_{N+1} = (\alpha - \hat{\alpha}) + (\beta - \hat{\beta}) x_{N+1} + u_{N+1} \qquad (4.20)$$

Now taking expectations through (4.20) we have that $E(Y_{N+1} - \hat{Y}_{N+1}) = 0$ since the OLS estimates of the intercept and the slope are unbiased and the expected value of the error is zero.

Next consider the variance of the prediction error. This can be written[3]:

$$E(Y_{N+1} - \hat{Y}_{N+1})^2 = \sigma_u^2 \left[1 + \frac{1}{N} + \frac{(x_{N+1} - \bar{x})^2}{\sum (x_i - \bar{x})^2} \right] \qquad (4.21)$$

Note that the prediction error variance changes according to the deviation of the right-hand side variable from its sample mean. The greater the discrepancy between the value of x used to construct the prediction and the sample mean of x, then the larger is the prediction error variance. What this means is that we are more likely to get accurate predictions when the value of the x variable used is a 'typical' value in the sense that it is close to the sample mean. The more extreme the value of x we use, i.e. the further from the sample mean, then the less reliable will be the prediction. The importance of this effect will vary depending on the nature of the data used.

---

[3] The derivation of the prediction error variance is straightforward but tedious and is therefore given in an appendix rather than in the main text.

Example: Suppose we wish to predict UK consumption growth under the assumption that GDP grows at 5%. Equation (4.19) will be the basis of our forecast and in addition we need the following items of information.

$$\hat{\sigma} = 1.41 \qquad \Delta\bar{y} = 2.50 \qquad \sum(\Delta y_i - \Delta\bar{y}) = 172.37$$

The central prediction is $\Delta\hat{c} = 0.69 + 0.83 \times 5.0 = 4.84$ and the prediction error variance is:

$$\hat{\sigma}^2 \left[1 + \frac{1}{N} + \frac{(5.0 - \Delta\bar{y})}{\sum(\Delta y_i - \Delta\bar{y})^2} \right] = 1.41^2 \left[1 + \frac{1}{46} + \frac{(5.0 - 2.5)^2}{172.37} \right] = 2.10$$

Given that the sample size is reasonably large we can use the normal distribution to construct the confidence interval. Therefore the lower and upper bounds for the 95% confidence interval are given by $4.84 - 1.96 \times \sqrt{2.10} = 2.00$ and $4.84 + 1.96 \times \sqrt{2.10} = 7.68$ respectively.

It is interesting to examine how the prediction error variance changes with the value of the right-hand side variable in this case. Figure 4.4 shows the scatter of points along with the regression line and a 95% confidence interval constructed by adding and subtracting twice the square root of the prediction error variance from the regression line. The curvature of the prediction error bands in this case is very slight.

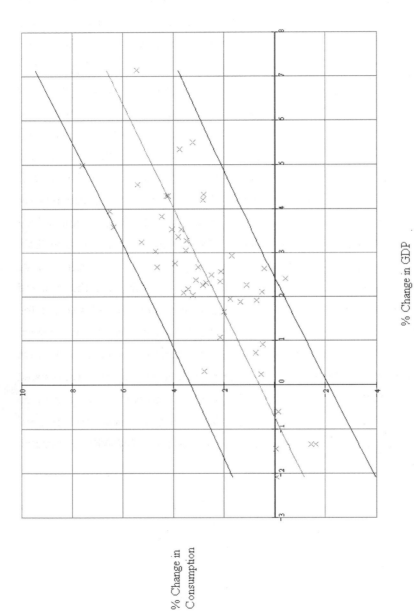

% Change in Consumption

% Change in GDP

Figure 4.4: Predictions and prediction error bands for the consumption model

4.7 Summary

In this chapter we have introduced one of the basic statistical tools of econometrics in the form of the linear regression model. We have shown that this can be derived straightforwardly from a simple calculus problem. In addition we have shown that, under certain assumptions, this estimator has desirable properties in that it is unbiased and has the smallest variance in the class of unbiased estimators. These assumptions, known as the *classical linear regression model assumptions* or alternatively the *Gauss-Markov assumptions* also allow us to determine the distribution of the least squares estimator and therefore to conduct hypothesis tests concerning the unknown parameters of the relationship between the Y and X variables which enter the regression model. However, it should be emphasised that the Gauss-Markov assumptions rarely hold in practice when estimating econometric models and we need to investigate further the implications of the failure of these assumptions and to develop techniques for dealing with such failure. This chapter has also developed further the idea of the power of a statistical test. Econometricians typically have little direct control over the power of the tests they use and therefore this is a topic which is often neglected. In later chapters we will see that the econometricians response to lack of power in tests is often to seek alternative (and better) tests rather than to increase the power of existing tests by generating more data. Finally, we have introduced the idea of prediction using the linear regression model and demonstrated that prediction involves both the construction of a central predicted value and some measure of uncertainty such as a confidence interval. The size of the confidence interval depends on the distance between the value of the right-hand side variable used to construct the prediction and the sample mean of this variable.

Appendix 4.1: Distribution of the OLS parameters

The focus of interest in the main text is the distribution of the OLS estimator of the slope coefficient. However, we also need to determine the distribution of the intercept estimator $\hat{\alpha}$. First we note that, from the least squares normal equations, we have:

$$\hat{\alpha} = \bar{Y} - \hat{\beta}\bar{X} = \alpha + \bar{X}\left(\beta - \hat{\beta}\right) + \bar{u} \tag{4.22}$$

Since $E\left(\hat{\beta}\right) = \beta$ and $E\left(\bar{u}\right) = 0$, it immediately follows that $E\left(\hat{\alpha}\right) = \alpha$, or that the OLS estimate of the intercept is unbiased. This result also illustrates the fact that, since the OLS estimator of α is a linear combination of normally distributed variables, it too, follows a normal distribution.

Next consider the variance of the OLS intercept estimator. Substituting (4.13) for $\hat{\beta}$ in (4.22) yields:

$$\hat{\alpha} = \alpha - \frac{\bar{X}\sum\left(X_i - \bar{X}\right)u_i}{\sum\left(X_i - \bar{X}\right)^2} + \bar{u} \tag{4.23}$$

Therefore the variance can be derived as:

$$V\left(\hat{\alpha}\right) = E\left(\hat{\alpha} - E\left(\hat{\alpha}\right)\right)^2 = E\left(-\frac{\bar{X}\sum\left(X_i - \bar{X}\right)u_i}{\sum\left(X_i - \bar{X}\right)^2} + \bar{u}\right)^2 \tag{4.24}$$

Expanding the term in brackets and applying the expectations operator[4] then yields:

---

[4] Note that this derivation makes use of the CLRM assumptions in the same way as the derivation of the variance of the slope coefficient estimator. Also note that the cross-product terms are eliminated by virtue of the fact that $\sum\left(X_i - \bar{X}\right) = 0$ by construction.

$$V(\hat{\alpha}) = \sigma_u^2 \left(\frac{1}{N} + \frac{\bar{X}^2}{\sum (X_i - \bar{X})^2} \right) \qquad (4.25)$$

For completeness, we can also derive the covariance of the slope and intercept estimates as:

$$\mathrm{cov}(\hat{\alpha}, \hat{\beta}) = E(\hat{\alpha} - E(\hat{\alpha}))(\hat{\beta} - E(\hat{\beta}))$$

$$\qquad (4.26)$$

$$= E\left(-\frac{\bar{X}\sum (X_i - \bar{X})u_i}{\sum (X_i - \bar{X})^2} + \bar{u} \right)\left(\frac{\sum (X_i - \bar{X})u_i}{\sum (X_i - \bar{X})^2} \right)$$

Multiplying out the parentheses and applying the expectations operator yields:

$$\mathrm{cov}(\hat{\alpha}, \hat{\beta}) = -\frac{\bar{X}}{\sum (X_i - \bar{X})^2} \sigma_u^2 \qquad (4.27)$$

Therefore the intercept and slope estimates for the OLS model can be shown to follow a joint normal distribution of the form:

$$\begin{pmatrix} \hat{\alpha} \\ \hat{\beta} \end{pmatrix} \sim N\left(\begin{pmatrix} \alpha \\ \beta \end{pmatrix}, \sigma_u^2 \begin{pmatrix} \dfrac{1}{N} + \dfrac{\bar{X}^2}{\sum (X_i - \bar{X})^2} & -\dfrac{\bar{X}}{\sum (X_i - \bar{X})^2} \\ -\dfrac{\bar{X}}{\sum (X_i - \bar{X})^2} & \dfrac{1}{\sum (X_i - \bar{X})^2} \end{pmatrix} \right) \qquad (4.28)$$

Appendix 4.2: Derivation of the prediction error variance

The prediction error variance is defined as:

$$E\left(Y_{N+1} - \hat{Y}_{N+1}\right)^2 = E\left(\alpha + \beta x_{N+1} + u_i - \hat{\alpha} - \hat{\beta} x_{N+1}\right)^2 \qquad (4.29)$$

Note that the right-hand side of this expression can be written:

$$E\left(\left(\alpha - \hat{\alpha}\right) + \left(\beta - \hat{\beta}\right)x_{N+1} + u_{N+1}\right)^2 \qquad (4.30)$$

Expanding this yields:

$$E\left(\begin{array}{c} \left(\alpha - \hat{\alpha}\right)^2 + \left(\beta - \hat{\beta}\right)^2 x_{N+1}^2 + u_{N+1}^2 + 2u_{N+1}\left(\alpha - \hat{\alpha}\right) + \\ 2u_{N+1}\left(\beta - \hat{\beta}\right)x_{N+1} + 2\left(\alpha - \hat{\alpha}\right)\left(\beta - \hat{\beta}\right)x_{N+1} \end{array}\right) \qquad (4.31)$$

Since $\operatorname{cov}\left(u_i u_{N+1}\right) = 0$; $i = 1, \ldots, N$ we have $E\left(u_{N+1}\left(\alpha - \hat{\alpha}\right)\right) = E\left(u_{N+1}\left(\beta - \hat{\beta}\right)\right) = 0$ and therefore taking expectations through (4.31) yields:

$$E\left(Y_{N+1} - \hat{Y}_{N+1}\right)^2 = \sigma_u^2\left[\frac{1}{N} + \frac{\bar{x}^2}{\sum\left(x_i - \bar{x}\right)^2}\right] + x_{N+1}^2 \frac{\sigma_u^2}{\sum\left(x_i - \bar{x}\right)^2} + \sigma_u^2$$

$$- \bar{x}\, x_{N+1} \frac{\sigma_u^2}{\sum\left(x_i - \bar{x}\right)^2} \qquad (4.32)$$

$$= \sigma_u^2\left[1 + \frac{1}{N} + \frac{\left(x_{N+1} - \bar{x}\right)^2}{\sum\left(x_i - \bar{x}\right)^2}\right]$$

Thus the forecasts error variance can be decomposed into a part due to random errors to the underlying relationship σ_u^2 and a part due to the variance of the parameter estimates

$$\sigma_u^2\left[\frac{1}{N} + \frac{\left(x_{N+1} - \bar{x}\right)^2}{\sum\left(x_i - \bar{x}\right)^2}\right].$$

Exercises for Chapter 4

These exercises make use of the workfile SHARES.IRG. This contains data for the share prices of a number of leading UK companies as well as the FTSE 100 share price index. The aim is to estimate the *market model* which relates the daily return on a particular share to the return on the market as a whole. Daily returns are defined as the percentage change in the value of the share or the overall market index. Thus the model we will estimate takes the form:

$$R_t^i = \alpha + \beta R_t^M + u_t^i$$

where $R_t^i = 100 \times \left(P_t^i - P_{t-1}^i \right) / P_{t-1}^i$ and $R_t^M = 100 \times \left(P_t^M - P_{t-1}^M \right) / P_{t-1}^M$. P_t^i is the price of share i at date t and P_t^M is the value of the market index at date t.

Exercise 1

If we estimate the market model for AstraZeneca shares then we obtain the following results:

```
Ordinary Least Squares Regression Results
Sample period: 2 to 1359
Dependent Variable DASTRA
Sample Size 1358
```

Variable	Coefficient	Std Err	T-Ratio
C	-0.008039	0.034037	-0.236183
DFTSE	0.891929	0.035108	25.405183

R-squared	0.3224	F-statistic	645.4233
SEE	1.253479	RSS	2130.563220
Durbin-Watson	1.7797	LogL	-2232.722030
ARCH(1) Test	5.4683	AIC	3.291195
Jarque-Bera	1519.7986	SIC	3.298874

a) Test the null hypothesis $H_0 : \beta = 0$ against the alternative $H_1 : \beta \neq 0$ using a 5% level of significance.

b) Test the null hypothesis $H_0 : \beta = 1$ against the alternative $H_1 : \beta < 1$ using a 5% level of significance.

c) Explain why the critical value you use in these two tests is different.

Exercise 2

An econometrician has estimated the following market model for British Airways shares:

```
Ordinary Least Squares Regression Results
Sample period: 2 to 1359
Dependent Variable DBA
Sample Size 1358

Variable          Coefficient        Std Err        T-Ratio

C                 2.742235 E-3       0.052921       0.051818
DM                1.523805           0.054585       27.915937

R-squared         0.3650        F-statistic         779.2996
SEE               1.948886      RSS             5150.302785
Durbin-Watson     2.0365        LogL           -2832.054370
ARCH(1) Test     16.3298        AIC                4.173865
Jarque-Bera     457.4844        SIC                4.181544
```

In addition we are given that the average value of DM is 0.035445 and $\sum \left(DM - \bar{DM} \right)^2 = 1274.731713$. A plot of the daily market returns for the sample period is given below:

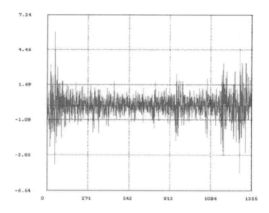

a) Calculate the predicted return on BA shares at the sample mean of the market return and calculate a 95% confidence interval for the prediction.

b) Identify (approximately!) the maximum values for the rise and fall of the FTSE during this period. Calculate the central predicted values for the change in BA shares as well as 95% confidence intervals based on these values? Are the confidence intervals noticeably higher than that calculated for the mean?

Exercise 3

Estimate the market model for Vodafone shares.

a) Test the null hypothesis $H_0 : \beta = 0$ against the alternative $H_1 : \beta \neq 0$ using a 5% level of significance.

b) Test the null hypothesis $H_0 : \beta = 1$. Is it sensible to use $H_1 : \beta < 1$ in this case? If not, suggest another alternative and use this for your test.

Chapter 5: The Multivariate Regression Model

5.1 Derivation of the multivariate OLS estimator

Multivariate regression analysis extends the model discussed in chapter 4 to the case where there are potentially many variables on the right-hand side of the model. For example, suppose we begin with a model of the form:

$$Y_i = \beta_1 + \beta_2 X_{i2} + \beta_3 X_{i3} + ... + \beta_k X_{ik} + u_i \tag{5.1}$$

in which we have data for each of the variables for a sample $i = 1, ..., N$. The residual sum of squares can be written:

$$RSS = \sum_{i=1}^{N} \left(Y_i - \hat{\beta}_1 - \hat{\beta}_2 X_{i2} - \hat{\beta}_3 X_{i3} - ... - \hat{\beta}_k X_{ik} \right)^2 \tag{5.2}$$

The OLS estimator is defined by taking the partial derivatives of (5.2) and setting them equal to zero to create a system of k equations in the k unknown parameters. This can be written:

$$N\hat{\beta}_1 + \sum X_{i2}\hat{\beta}_2 + ... + \sum X_{ik}\hat{\beta}_k = \sum Y_i$$
$$\sum X_{i2}\hat{\beta}_1 + \sum X_{i2}^2\hat{\beta}_2 + ... + \sum X_{i2}X_{ik}\hat{\beta}_k = \sum X_{i2}Y_i$$
$$..$$
$$\sum X_{ik}\hat{\beta}_1 + \sum X_{ik}X_{i2}\hat{\beta}_2 + ... + \sum X_{ik}^2\hat{\beta}_k = \sum X_{ik}Y_i \tag{5.3}$$

A much simpler derivation of the OLS estimator can be obtained by rewriting the model in matrix form. For example, we can write (5.1) in matrix form as:

$$y = X\beta + u \tag{5.4}$$

where y is an $N \times 1$ vector of observations for the endogenous variable, X is an $N \times k$ matrix whose first column consists of ones and whose other columns are the observations for each of the exogenous variables in turn, β is a $k \times 1$ vector of parameters and u is an $N \times 1$ vector of random errors.

To derive the OLS estimator we know specify a loss function consisting of the following quadratic form:

$$RSS = \left(y - X\hat{\beta} \right)' \left(y - X\hat{\beta} \right) = y'y + \hat{\beta}'X'X\hat{\beta} - 2\hat{\beta}' X'y \tag{5.5}$$

Differentiating with respect to $\hat{\beta}$ and setting the derivative equal to zero yields:

$$\left(X'X \right)\hat{\beta} = X'y \tag{5.6}$$

Equation (5.6) is the matrix form of the least squares normal equations. A comparison of the simplicity and elegance of equation (5.6) with the equivalent scalar expression (5.3) should convince the reader of the value of using the matrix form of the model. Another advantage of this form of the model is that it makes the conditions for the existence of a solution to the normal equations transparent. For a solution to exist we require $\left(X'X \right)$ to be invertible. This in turn requires the matrix X to have rank k i.e. there must be no linear dependent relationships between the columns of X.

If we assume that a solution to (5.6) exists then it takes the form:

$$\hat{\beta} = \left(X'X \right)^{-1} X'y \tag{5.7}$$

This form of the solution is considerably more elegant than that obtained through scalar algebra thus again illustrating the value of the matrix approach.

Example: The following example sets out the procedures by which a multivariate regression equation is constructed. The model estimated can be thought of as a demand curve for gasoline for the US economy and the data are annual observations from the period 1950 to 2004.

Our estimating equation takes the form:

$$Y_t = \beta_1 + \beta_2 X_{t2} + \beta_3 X_{t3} + u_t \tag{5.8}$$

Y is the first difference of the logarithm of consumption of gasoline measured in millions of barrels, X_2 is the first difference of the logarithm of gross domestic product in \$bn at 2000 prices, X_3 is the first difference of the logarithm of the ratio of the price index for gasoline and the GDP deflator and u is a random error.

From the data we obtain the following set of sample moments:

$$
\begin{aligned}
&\bar{X}_2 = 0.03426 \quad \bar{X}_3 = 0.0001857 \; \bar{Y} = 0.02413 \\
&\sum \left(X_{t2} - \bar{X}_2 \right)^2 = 0.02827 \\
&\sum \left(X_{t3} - \bar{X}_3 \right)^2 = 0.4387 \\
&\sum \left(X_{t2} - \bar{X}_2 \right)\left(X_{t3} - \bar{X}_3 \right) = -0.01339 \\
&\sum \left(X_{t2} - \bar{X}_2 \right)\left(Y_t - \bar{Y} \right) = 0.01902 \\
&\sum \left(X_{t3} - \bar{X}_3 \right)\left(Y_t - \bar{Y} \right) = -0.06276
\end{aligned}
\tag{5.9}
$$

The slope coefficients for this regression equation can therefore be calculated as:

$$\begin{pmatrix} \hat{\beta}_2 \\ \hat{\beta}_3 \end{pmatrix} = \begin{pmatrix} 0.02827 & -0.01339 \\ -0.01339 & 0.4387 \end{pmatrix}^{-1} \begin{pmatrix} 0.01902 \\ -0.06276 \end{pmatrix}$$
$$= \begin{pmatrix} 0.614 \\ -0.124 \end{pmatrix}$$

(5.10)

An estimate of the intercept can then be obtained by using the condition that the regression line must pass through the sample means of the data. This yields:

$$\hat{\beta}_1 = 0.02413 - 0.614 \times 0.03426 + 0.124 \times 0.0001857$$
$$= 0.00310$$

(5.11)

5.2 Derivation of the distribution of the OLS estimator

In order to derive the distribution of the multivariate OLS estimator, we must first set out the matrix equivalents of the CLRM assumptions set out in chapter 3. These are listed in Table 5.1:

Assumption 1:	The errors have zero mean:
	$E(\boldsymbol{u}) = \boldsymbol{0}$.
Assumptions 2 and 3:	The errors are serially independent and have constant variance:
	$E(\boldsymbol{u}\boldsymbol{u}') = \sigma_u^2 \boldsymbol{I}_N$
Assumption 4:	The right-hand side variables are exogenous:
	(a) Strong Form - $\boldsymbol{X}$ is fixed in repeated sample
	(b) Weak Form - $E(\boldsymbol{X}'\boldsymbol{u}) = \boldsymbol{0}$
Assumption 5:	The errors follow a normal distribution:
	$\boldsymbol{u} \sim N\left(0, \sigma_u^2 \boldsymbol{I}_N\right)$

Table 5.1 Assumptions of the Classical Linear Regression Model

Given the assumptions in Table 5.1, we can derive the distribution of the OLS estimator. First consider its mean – we have $\hat{\boldsymbol{\beta}} = (\boldsymbol{X}'\boldsymbol{X})^{-1} \boldsymbol{X}'\boldsymbol{y}$, substituting for $\boldsymbol{y}$ yields $\hat{\boldsymbol{\beta}} = \boldsymbol{\beta} + (\boldsymbol{X}'\boldsymbol{X})^{-1} \boldsymbol{X}'\boldsymbol{u}$. From assumption 4(a) we have that the only stochastic element in this expression is the vector of random errors $\boldsymbol{u}$. Therefore taking expectations yields $E(\hat{\boldsymbol{\beta}}) = \boldsymbol{\beta} + (\boldsymbol{X}'\boldsymbol{X})^{-1} \boldsymbol{X}'E(\boldsymbol{u})$ and by assumption 1 we have $E(\boldsymbol{u}) = \boldsymbol{0}$ which ensures that $E(\hat{\boldsymbol{\beta}}) = \boldsymbol{\beta}$ or that OLS is unbiased. Note also that by assumption 5 the OLS estimator is a linear combination of normally distributed random variables and is therefore itself normally distributed. It follows that the only thing left to do is to derive the variance of $\hat{\boldsymbol{\beta}}$ and we will have fully characterised its distribution.

To derive the variance of the OLS estimator we first note that the variance in the multivariate case will consist of a $k \times k$ symmetric matrix with variances of the individual OLS coefficient estimates on the diagonal and their covariances off the diagonal. Since we have demonstrated unbiasedness we can write:

$$\text{var}\left(\hat{\beta}\right) = E\left(\hat{\beta} - \beta\right)\left(\hat{\beta} - \beta\right)'$$
$$= E\left(X'X\right)^{-1} X'uu'X\left(X'X\right)^{-1}$$

(5.12)

Assumption 4(a) allows us to write the right-hand side of this expression as $\left(X'X\right)^{-1} X'E\left(uu'\right)X\left(X'X\right)^{-1}$. From assumptions 2 and 3 of the CLRM we have that $E\left(uu'\right) = \sigma_u^2 I_N$ and therefore with some minor algebra this yields:

$$\text{var}\left(\hat{\beta}\right) = \sigma_u^2 \left(X'X\right)^{-1}$$

(5.13)

Again note that the use of matrix algebra permits a considerable improvement in terms of the elegance of the notation and the ease of the derivation. By the use of a few lines of algebra, we have been able to show that, under the CLRM assumptions:

$$\hat{\beta} \sim N\left(\beta, \sigma_u^2 \left(X'X\right)^{-1}\right)$$

(5.14)

The derivation of the distribution of the OLS estimator would have taken up far more space and would have involved far more complex expressions if we have retained the use of scalar notation. Thus the initial costs of writing the model in matrix form are arguably more than justified in terms of the subsequent ease with which we can derive important results for the OLS estimator.

5.3 Hypothesis testing in the multivariate regression model

We have seen that testing a hypothesis requires the following – (1) a null and an alternative hypothesis, (2) a test statistic whose distribution is known under the null and (3) a decision rule for acceptance/rejection of the null hypothesis. The main difference between testing in the bivariate regression model and in the multivariate regression model is that we have a greater variety of null hypotheses of interest. We will consider three cases of interest: the first is where we wish to test a hypothesis relating to a single coefficient, the second is where we wish to test a hypothesis which relates two or more coefficients and the third is where we wish to test several hypotheses simultaneously.

5.3.1 Testing a hypothesis relating to a single coefficient

Suppose we wish to test $H_0 : \beta_j = \bar{\beta}_j$ against the alternative $H_1 : \beta_j \neq \bar{\beta}_j$. From (5.14) we have that $\hat{\beta}_j \sim N\left(\bar{\beta}_j, \sigma_u^2 \varsigma_{jj}\right)$ under the null – where ς_{jj} is the (j,j)th element of the matrix $\left(X'X\right)^{-1}$. If σ_u^2 was known then we could use $\hat{\beta}_j - \bar{\beta}_j / \sigma_u \sqrt{\varsigma_{jj}}$ as our test statistic since this would follow the standard normal distribution. The problem is that σ_u^2 is typically not known . Therefore we replace σ_u with the estimate $\hat{\sigma}_u = \sqrt{\sum\left(Y_i - \hat{Y}_i\right)^2 / \left(N - k\right)}$. This means that our test statistic becomes:

$$t = \frac{\hat{\beta}_j - \bar{\beta}_j}{\hat{\sigma}_u \sqrt{\varsigma_{jj}}} \tag{5.15}$$

which follows the t distribution with N-k degrees of freedom under the null. We can then compare (5.15) with an appropriate critical value from the t_{N-k} distribution tables to make a decision as to whether to accept or reject the null hypothesis.

Example: Continuing the example from section 5.1, we need to calculate the variance-covariance matrix of the coefficients in order to perform hypothesis tests. Given $RSS = 0.01956$ we have:

$$V\begin{pmatrix} \hat{\beta}_2 \\ \hat{\beta}_3 \end{pmatrix} = \hat{\sigma}_u^2 \begin{pmatrix} 0.02827 & -0.01339 \\ -0.01339 & 0.4387 \end{pmatrix}^{-1}$$

$$= \hat{\sigma}_u^2 \begin{pmatrix} 35.892 & 1.095 \\ 1.095 & 2.313 \end{pmatrix} \tag{5.16}$$

Suppose, for example, that we want to test the null hypothesis $H_0 : \beta_2 = 1$ against the alternative $H_1 : \beta_2 < 1$. The test statistic is $(0.641 - 1)/(0.0194\sqrt{35.892}) = -3.1$ (note that $\hat{\sigma}_u = \sqrt{0.000376} = 0.0194$ is the *standard error of the regression*). The 5% critical value for a one-tailed t-statistic with 52 degrees of freedom is -1.675, therefore we reject the null hypothesis in favour of the alternative at the 5% level. Alternatively we can calculate the p-value of the test statistic as 0.00019 which again indicates that we should reject the null at most reasonable levels of significance.

5.3.2 Testing a hypothesis which relates several coefficients

In multivariate regression models we often wish to test hypothesis which relate several of the model's parameters. A typical example of this is where we wish to test the hypothesis that two coefficients have equal but opposite sign. Hypotheses of this type can be written as linear combinations of the model parameters. For example, in equation (5.1) we might want to test the null hypothesis $H_0 : \beta_2 = \alpha\beta_3$ against the alternative $H_1 : \beta_2 \neq \alpha\beta_3$ where α is a non-zero number. Following the discussion in the previous section, we could write a test statistic for this hypothesis as:

$$\frac{\hat{\beta}_2 - \alpha\hat{\beta}_3}{\sqrt{\operatorname{var}\left(\hat{\beta}_2 - \alpha\hat{\beta}_3\right)}} \sim t_{N-k} \tag{5.17}$$

The problem of course is obtaining an estimate of $\operatorname{var}\left(\hat{\beta}_2 - \alpha\hat{\beta}_3\right)$. Returning to the definition of a variance, we have:

$$E\left(\hat{\beta}_2 - \alpha\hat{\beta}_3\right)^2 = \operatorname{var}\left(\hat{\beta}_2\right) + \alpha^2 \operatorname{var}\left(\hat{\beta}_3\right) - 2\alpha\operatorname{cov}\left(\hat{\beta}_2, \hat{\beta}_3\right) \tag{5.18}$$

Therefore, when we test hypotheses which relate different model parameters, the relevant variance depends on the off-diagonal elements of the variance-covariance matrix.

Example: Suppose we wish to test the null hypothesis $H_0 : \beta_2 = -\beta_3$ against the alternative $H_1 : \beta_2 \neq \beta_3$ in the gasoline demand model we estimated earlier. This is not necessarily an interesting economic hypothesis but it will serve to illustrate the statistical procedure.

The test statistic in this case can be written as:

$$t = \frac{\hat{\beta}_2 + \hat{\beta}_3}{se\left(\hat{\beta}_2 + \hat{\beta}_3\right)} \tag{5.19}$$

which, under the null hypothesis, follows a t-distribution with 52 degrees of freedom. From (5.18) we have that:

$$V\left(\hat{\beta}_2 + \hat{\beta}_3\right) = \frac{0.01986}{56-3}\left(35.892 + 2.313 - 2 \times 1.095\right)$$
$$= 0.0152$$

Using the parameter values calculated earlier we therefore have:

$$t = \frac{0.614 - 0.124}{\sqrt{0.0152}} = 3.97 \tag{5.20}$$

Since the test statistic is greater than the 5% critical value for t_{52} we reject the null in this case.

5.3.3 Testing several restrictions simultaneously

With multivariate regression we often wish to test a number of restrictions simultaneously. For example, if our model is (5.1) then we might wish to test $H_0 : \beta_2 = \bar{\beta}_2, \beta_3 = \bar{\beta}_3$ against the alternative $H_1 : \beta_2 \neq \bar{\beta}_2$ and/or $\beta_3 \neq \bar{\beta}_3$. Joint hypotheses of this type require the use of an F test. To calculate a test statistic we run separate regressions, one imposing the restrictions given in the null hypothesis and one allowing the regression coefficients to be freely determined. This generates two values of the residual sum of squares. The *restricted residual sum of squares* is calculated with the restrictions imposed i.e. $RRSS = RSS\left(\beta_2 = \bar{\beta}_2, \beta_3 = \bar{\beta}_3\right)$ and the *unrestricted residual sum of squares* used the OLS estimated values for these coefficients $URSS = RSS\left(\beta_2 = \hat{\beta}_2, \beta_3 = \hat{\beta}_3\right)$. The F test is based on a comparison of these residual sums of squares. In particular, under the null hypothesis, we have:

$$F = \frac{\left(RRSS - URSS\right)/r}{URSS/\left(N-k\right)} \sim F_{r,N-k} \tag{5.21}$$

where r is the number of restrictions we impose. Note that $RRSS \geq URSS$, therefore F must always be weakly positive.

Example: Suppose we wish to test the following joint null hypothesis for our gasoline demand model $H_0 : \beta_2 = 1, \beta_3 = -1$ against $H_1 : \beta_2 \neq 1$ and/or $\beta_3 \neq -1$. The $RRSS$ is calculated as 0.369263 and the $URSS$ is calculated as 0.019564. Therefore the test statistic is:

$$F = \frac{\left(0.369263 - 0.019564\right)/2}{0.019564/52} = 464.74 \tag{5.22}$$

Under the null hypothesis this is distributed as $F_{2,52}$ and the 5% critical value for this distribution is 3.175. Therefore since the test statistic is greater than the critical value we reject the null at the 5% level.

The joint test of linear restrictions described above has an important special case. This is the test of the joint significance of the regression coefficients i.e. a test of

$H_0: \beta_2 = \beta_3 = ... \beta_k = 0$ against the alternative that one or more regression coefficients is different from zero. Under the null hypothesis we have that:

$$F = \frac{(TSS - RSS)/(k-1)}{RSS/(N-k)} \sim F_{k-1, N-k} \qquad (5.23)$$

where TSS is the sum of squared deviations of the y variable from its mean and RSS is the residual sum of squares from the regression. This is the F-test which is frequently reported as part of the regression output of most packages.

5.4 Goodness of fit

So far we have concentrated on the issue of hypothesis testing in the regression model. A related topic is the extent to which a regression model can be said to 'explain' the variation in the data. This is the issue of goodness of fit.

To analyse goodness of fit we first need to introduce the idea of *analysis of variation*. For any variable Y we can divide up the variation into three parts: these are the total variation, the explained variation and the residual variation. In order to analyse the contribution of the model to an explanation of the data we define the following sums of squares:

$$
\begin{aligned}
TSS &= \sum (Y_i - \bar{Y})^2 \\
ESS &= \sum (\hat{Y}_i - \bar{Y})^2 \\
RSS &= \sum (Y_i - \hat{Y}_i)^2
\end{aligned}
\qquad (5.24)
$$

TSS is the total sum of squares and consists of the sum of the squared deviations of the observations of Y from their sample mean value, ESS is the explained sum of squares and consists of the sum of the squared deviations of the fitted values from the regression equation from the sample mean of the data and, finally, RSS is the residual sum of squares which consists of the sum of the squared deviations of the observations of Y from the fitted values. Some simple algebra confirms that $TSS = ESS + RSS$, i.e. the total sum of squares consists of the sum of the explained and residual sums of squares.

5.4.1 The coefficient of determination – R-squared

A natural way to measure the goodness of fit of an equation is to calculate the proportion of the total sum of squares which is accounted for by the regression. This gives the statistic known as the coefficient of determination or R-squared for a regression model. It can be written in two alternative ways as shown in equation (5.25).

$$R^2 = \frac{ESS}{TSS} = 1 - \frac{RSS}{TSS} \qquad (5.25)$$

The definition of R-squared implies a number of important properties. First, it is obvious that this statistic is bounded between zero and one. Since ESS and TSS are both positive numbers and $ESS \leq TSS$. Second, the closer R-squared is to one then the more of the variation of y which is explained by the model and therefore the better is the fit of the model.

If R-squared measures goodness of fit and increasing R-squared means an increase in fit, then should we always seek to choose a model which has the maximum value for this statistic? There are at least two reasons why this may be an unwise strategy. The first is that R-squared can always be increased by the addition of extra variables on the right-hand side of the regression equation – even if these are irrelevant to an explanation of the behaviour of the variable in question. Thus a strategy of maximising R-squared will lead to models which are 'over-fitted', i.e. include too many explanatory variables. The second reason is that the value of R-squared can depend on the way in which the regression equation is written (see the example which follows) and this can lead the inexperienced researcher to judge that one model fits 'better' than another even when there is no difference between the two.

Example: Using our model of US demand for gasoline, we obtain the following sums of squares: $TSS = 0.0391$ and $RSS = 0.0196$, it follows that the R-squared for this regression can be calculated as $R^2 = 1 - 0.0196 / 0.0391 = 0.499$. We can interpret this as telling us that about 50% of the variation in the left-hand side variable is being explained by the model.

Now, consider what happens when we add an unrelated random variable as an extra regressor. The regression obtained is given in equation (5.26):

$$\Delta g_t = \underset{(0.0048)}{0.0029} + \underset{(0.117)}{0.6148} \, \Delta y_t - \underset{(0.0296)}{0.1238} \, \Delta p_t + \underset{(0.0029)}{0.0024} \, z_t + \hat{u}_t \qquad (5.26)$$
$$RSS = 0.0193$$

Note that the unrelated variable z is statistically insignificant with a t-ratio of $0.0024 / 0.0029 = 0.83$. However, the residual sum of squares is lower than calculated previously and therefore the R-squared also falls. In this case we have $R^2 = 1 - 0.0193 / 0.0391 = 0.506$.

Next, consider what happens if we write the regression equation in a different form. Rather than regress the change in gasoline demand on the right-hand side variables, we regress the level of gasoline demand on the same right-hand side variables plus the lagged gasoline demand with a restricted coefficient value of one. This produces identical coefficient estimates as shown below in equation (5.27). However, the R-squared appears to increase substantially. The reason for this is that we now have a different left-hand side variable. The model 'explains' substantially more of the variation of the level of this series than it 'explains' the variation in its growth rate.

$$g_t = g_{t-1} + 0.00312 + 0.6141\,\Delta y_t - 0.1243\,\Delta p_t + \hat{u}_t$$
$$\qquad\qquad (0.0048)\quad (0.116)\qquad (0.029)$$

$$TSS = 6.3514 \qquad\qquad RSS = 0.01956 \quad R^2 = 0.997$$

(5.27)

5.4.2 Other measures of goodness of fit

Although the *R*-squared statistic is the most frequently quoted measure of goodness of fit, most regression packages produce a range of other statistics. These are designed to deal with the pitfalls of the *R*-squared statistic in a variety of ways.

Perhaps the simplest alternative measure of goodness of fit is the *standard error of the regression*. This is calculated as the square root of the residual sum of squares divided by the number of degrees of freedom available, i.e.

$$\hat{\sigma} = \sqrt{\frac{\sum\left(Y_i - \hat{Y}_i\right)^2}{N - k}}$$

(5.28)

This statistic cannot provide an absolute measure of goodness of fit since it is measured in the same units as the data series itself. However, what it can do is provide a basis for comparison of different models which is not sensitive to the way in which the models are written. For example, the standard error of the regression for (5.27) is 0.0194 and this remains unchanged if we transform the model by subtracting g_{t-1} from both sides of the equation and thus estimating a model which has differenced data rather than levels data on the left-hand side.

Another measure of goodness of fit is the *adjusted R-squared statistic* or *R-bar squared*. This is designed to deal with the problem that the standard *R*-squared statistic always increases when we add variables to the model – even if these are irrelevant and statistically insignificant. The adjusted *R*-squared statistic is defined as:

$$\bar{R}^2 = 1 - \left(1 - R^2\right)\frac{N-1}{N-k} \qquad (5.29)$$

Effectively the adjusted R-squared statistic penalises the addition of irrelevant variables to the model. Unlike the simple R-squared statistic it will fall in value if additional variables are not sufficiently significant. In extreme cases the adjusted R-squared statistic can become negative.

Other goodness of fit statistics are based on transformations of the log-likelihood statistic. The log-likelihood is defined as:

$$LL = -\frac{N}{2}\left(1 + \ln\left(2\pi\right) + \ln\left(\frac{RSS}{N}\right)\right) \qquad (5.30)$$

The log-likelihood is a function of the residual sum of squares and therefore the behaviour of this function, as we alter the specification of the regression equation, mirrors the behaviour of the residual sum of squares. In particular, it follows that since the log-likelihood is a decreasing function of the residual sum of squares, and that the residual sum of squares increases as we add extra variables, the value of the log-likelihood must always *increase* as we expand the number of explanatory variables.

Choosing a model which maximises the log-likelihood statistic will lead to over-fitting since the inclusion of irrelevant variables can only act to increase its value. However, a number of statistics based on the log-likelihood have been suggested as ways of selecting one model from a range of alternatives. Two of the most commonly reported transformations of the log-likelihood are the *Akaike Information Criterion* (AIC) and the *Schwartz Information Criterion* (SIC). The AIC is defined as:

103

$$AIC = -\frac{2}{N}(LL - k) \qquad (5.31)$$

while the SIC is defined as:

$$SIC = -\frac{2}{N}\left(LL - \frac{k\ln(N)}{2}\right) \qquad (5.32)$$

Note that in both these cases the statistics are defined in such a way that a lower value implies a model which fits the data better. In each case the inclusion of the k terms in the definition of the test statistic penalises the addition of irrelevant or insignificant variables. As k increases (the number of variables on the right-hand side of the regression increases) then the LL increases leading to a fall in both AIC and SIC. However, this may not be enough to offset the increasing effect on these statistics caused by the direct effect of k in equations (5.31) and (5.32). The SIC penalises the addition of irrelevant variables more than AIC and will generally lead to the choice of a more *parsimonious* model, i.e. one which contains fewer explanatory variables.

Example: Consider the following two equations for gasoline consumption in the US. Each is estimated over the period 1951 to 2004. The only difference is that the second equation includes the lagged growth rate of US GDP as well as the current rate.

$$\Delta g_t = \underset{(0.0048)}{0.0043} + \underset{(0.120)}{0.5629}\,\Delta y_t - \underset{(0.0292)}{0.1252}\,\Delta p_t + \hat{u}_t$$

$$R^2 = 0.472 \qquad \bar{R}^2 = 0.452 \qquad\qquad \hat{\sigma} = 0.0192 \qquad (5.33)$$
$$LL = 138.4 \qquad AIC = -5.013 \qquad\qquad SIC = -4.903$$

$$\Delta g_t = \underset{(0.0059)}{0.0026} + \underset{(0.122)}{0.5554}\,\Delta y_t - \underset{(0.0297)}{0.1271}\,\Delta p_t + \underset{(0.117)}{0.0564}\,\Delta y_{t-1} + \hat{u}_t$$

$$R^2 = 0.475 \qquad \bar{R}^2 = 0.443 \qquad\qquad \hat{\sigma} = 0.0194 \qquad (5.34)$$
$$LL = 138.5 \qquad AIC = -4.981 \qquad\qquad SIC = -4.833$$

If we compare these equations we see that the additional variable has a t-ratio of 0.48 and is therefore insignificant at any standard level. However, its addition produces an increase in both R-squared and the log-likelihood. Choosing a model on the basis of either of these statistics is therefore likely to lead to over-fitting. The other goodness of fit statistics produce a more reliable basis for model selection. The standard error of the regression increases when we add the extra variable due to the fact that the loss of one degree of freedom is more than enough to offset a small fall in the residual sum of squares. Similarly the adjusted R-squared statistic falls in (5.34) reflecting the lower degrees of freedom. Finally, both AIC and SIC are lower for the simpler or more parsimonious model (5.33) indicating that we would choose this model rather than (5.34).

5.4.3 Goodness of fit and significance of the regressors

The R-squared for a regression equation is closely related to the F-statistic for the joint significance of the regressors. To see this consider the following definition of the F-statistic:

$$F = \frac{(TSS - RSS)/(k-1)}{RSS/(N-k)} \tag{5.35}$$

Using this definition, we can think of the F statistic as a test of k-1 linear restrictions $\beta_2 = \beta_3 = ... = \beta_k = 0$. TSS is the restricted sum of squares when all the slope coefficients are set to zero whereas RSS is the unrestricted sum of squares when all the slope coefficients are freely estimated. Now, we can also rewrite (5.35) as shown below and then transform it by dividing numerator and denominator by TSS:

$$F = \frac{ESS}{TSS - ESS}\left(\frac{N-k}{k-1}\right) = \frac{R^2}{1-R^2}\left(\frac{N-k}{k-1}\right) \tag{5.36}$$

Therefore we can show that the F statistic and R-squared have an exact algebraic relationship. Moreover, it is straightforward to show that an increase in F will always produce an increase in R-squared.

5.5 Misspecification

There are two main kinds of misspecification we need to consider. The first case is when we omit a relevant variable from our model and the second is when we include an irrelevant variable. The first case produces bias in the coefficient estimates for the remaining variables while the second produces unbiased, but inefficient, estimates.

Consider the case in which the 'true' model takes the form $Y_i = \beta_1 X_{i1} + \beta_2 X_{i2} + u_i$. If we omit the X_2 variable from the model then the effect is that the error term becomes $v_i = \beta_2 X_{i2} + u_i$. The OLS estimator of the β_1 coefficient takes the form:

$$\hat{\beta}_1 = \frac{\sum X_{i1} Y_i}{\sum X_{i1}^2} = \beta_1 + \beta_2 \frac{\sum X_{i1} X_{i2}}{\sum X_{i1}^2} + \frac{\sum X_{i1} u_i}{\sum X_{i1}^2} \qquad (5.37)$$

Taking expectations through (5.37) demonstrates that $E\left(\hat{\beta}_1\right) \neq \beta_1$ unless $\beta_2 = 0$ (in which case X_2 should not have been in the model in the first place) or $\sum X_{i1} X_{i2} = 0$, i.e. the correlation between the X variables is equal to zero. Therefore, except in very special cases, the omission of a relevant variable from the regression will lead to biased estimates of the remaining coefficients.

Given that leaving out relevant variables produces bias, it is tempting to adopt a strategy of including as many variables as possible to reduce the chance of accidentally introducing bias into our equation. However, this strategy also has its pitfalls. The problem we have is that, when the explanatory variables are *collinear* the inclusion of extra right-hand side variables increases the variance of the OLS estimates thus leading to inefficiency. Inefficiency of this kind is often described as *multicollinearity*. This can lead to problems even when we have a correctly specified model in that collinearity between the right-hand side variables inevitably leads to some loss of efficiency.

Variables in a regression equation are said to be collinear if they are correlated with each other. A certain degree of collinearity is present in almost all econometric models since it is very rarely the case that the right-hand side variables of a model are completely uncorrelated (or orthogonal). However, collinearity becomes a serious problem if the extent of it is such that the X matrix has rank less than k where k is the number of columns. Alternatively, if the X matrix has rank less than k then at least one of the eigenvalues of the $(X'X)$ matrix will be zero. Under these circumstances $(X'X)$ is not invertible and we cannot calculate the OLS estimator. Examples of situations in which this arises are when one variable is simply a scaled version of another ($X_m = \phi X_n$; $m \neq n$) or when a linear combination of a subset of variables equals one of the other variables of the model. If either of these two situations is the case then the OLS procedure breaks down.

The situations described in the previous paragraph can be defined as perfect collinearity. A less fatal, but still serious situation, could occur if two variables were very highly but not perfectly correlated. For example, we might have $X_m = \phi X_n + \varepsilon_t$ where σ_ε^2 was very small. OLS estimates could be calculated in this case but the correlation between the X variables would render these estimates extremely imprecise. This situation has been termed the multicollinearity problem.

Consider the following regression model with two variables on the right hand side of the equation:

$$Y_i = \beta_1 + \beta_2 X_{i1} + \beta_3 X_{i3} + u_i \qquad (5.38)$$

The variance-covariance matrix of the slope coefficients of the OLS estimator can be written:

$$V\left(\hat{\beta}\right)=\sigma_u^2\left(\begin{array}{cc}\sum\left(X_{i2}-\bar{X}_2\right)^2 & \sum\left(X_{i2}-\bar{X}_2\right)\left(X_{i3}-\bar{X}_3\right) \\ \sum\left(X_{i2}-\bar{X}_2\right)\left(X_{i3}-\bar{X}_3\right) & \sum\left(X_{i3}-\bar{X}_3\right)^2\end{array}\right)^{-1}$$

(5.39)

$$=\frac{\sigma_u^2}{\Delta}\left(\begin{array}{cc}\sum\left(X_{i3}-\bar{X}_3\right)^2 & -\sum\left(X_{i2}-\bar{X}_2\right)\left(X_{i3}-\bar{X}_3\right) \\ -\sum\left(X_{i2}-\bar{X}_2\right)\left(X_{i3}-\bar{X}_3\right) & \sum\left(X_{i2}-\bar{X}_2\right)^2\end{array}\right)$$

where $\Delta=\sum\left(X_{i2}-\bar{X}_2\right)^2\sum\left(X_{i3}-\bar{X}_3\right)^2-\left(\sum\left(X_{i2}-\bar{X}_2\right)\left(X_{i3}-\bar{X}_3\right)\right)^2$ is the determinant of the cross-product matrix $\left(X'X\right)$. Now it is easy to see that $\Delta=\sum\left(X_{i2}-\bar{X}_2\right)^2\sum\left(X_{i3}-\bar{X}_3\right)^2\left(1-\hat{\rho}^2\right)$ where $\hat{\rho}$ is the sample correlation coefficient between the X_2 and X_3 variables. It follows that as the correlation coefficient gets close to one, then Δ gets close to zero. Since the variance-covariance matrix is a multiple of $1/\Delta$ it also follows that the variances of the OLS estimator will increase in size.

To some extent multicollinearity is always present in econometric analysis. Economic data is rarely experimental and, as a result, different variables in the same regression model are usually correlated with each other. However, multicollinearity only becomes a serious problem when this correlation becomes very high. The main symptoms of a serious multicollinearity problem are individually insignificant variables (low t-ratios) coupled with a high degree of joint significance (high values of R-squared and the F statistic). If such symptoms are detected then examination of the covariance matrix of the right-hand side variables can prove useful in identifying which variables are most closely related.

Perfect multicollinearity – in which there is an exact linear relationship between a subset of right-hand side variables – is rarely encountered in correctly specified models but can easily be introduced accidentally into a model. For example, if we have four separate quarterly dummy variables in a time series regression, then their sum will equal one. If we also include a constant term then there is a perfectly collinear relationship between this group of variables. Examples like this, in which the introduction of dummy variables produces perfect collinearity, are remarkably easy to generate in applied work. Most regression packages will generate an error message in cases like this – usually of the form 'Near Singular Matrix' – and fail to generate any regression estimates. However, some non-specialist software may still produce an 'answer' with the symptoms of severe multicollinearity.

5.6 Interpreting a regression equation

We have now developed the statistical tools necessary to conduct a preliminary evaluation of a regression equation. To complete this chapter we will look at the output of a typical regression package (EViews) and discuss how we can interpret the results in a systematic and sensible manner.

Figure 5.1 shows a typical set of regression results – in this case we have reproduced the I-REG regression results for the gasoline demand equation which has been used as an example throughout this chapter. To interpret these results we need to address two separate but related issues – the first is the extent to which the equation has a sensible economic interpretation and the second is the extent to which the equation exhibits a reasonable statistical fit to the data.

5.6.1 Economic interpretation

The most important question we need to ask when examining an estimated equation is whether the signs and magnitudes of the coefficient estimates are consistent with our expectations from economic theory. In this case we are estimating what amounts to a demand relationship and hence we would expect to find a positive effect of income (GDP) and a negative effect of price (the ratio of gasoline price to the GDP deflator). Both estimated coefficients have their expected signs so our equation is at least sensible from this perspective.

In addition to the signs of the regression coefficients we also need to consider their magnitudes. The equation is estimated in log-linear form and therefore the coefficient estimates are elasticities. The coefficient estimate for DLOG(GDP) of 0.61 therefore indicates that a 1% point increase in the growth rate of GDP will increase the growth rate of gasoline demand by 0.61% points. This is a 'reasonable' magnitude in the sense that it does not lead to obviously absurd results. For example, a coefficient of 500 would be clearly ridiculous in that it would imply a huge response of demand to a very small change in the scale variable. Similarly, a coefficient of 0.01 – although positive – would indicate a magnitude of response well below what a passing knowledge of this market would regard as reasonable. The coefficient estimate for DLOG(PGAS/PDEF) of -0.12 is also reasonable in that it indicates a negative response of demand to relative price with a magnitude which is within plausible bounds.

If you have read this far then you should have realised by now that assessment of an econometric equation embodies some of the qualities of an art rather than an exact science. The investigator needs to have some idea in advance of what constitutes a 'reasonable' model. Models with parameter estimates outside the band of 'reasonableness' can usually be rejected – either because the underling theory has been proved inadequate or because there has been some statistical flaw in the calculation or estimation of the equation in question. However, it is rarely the case that economic theory provides hypotheses which are sufficiently tightly defined for the investigator to accept or reject a model without some degree of individual judgement.

5.6.2 Statistical assessment of an equation

When it comes to the statistical assessment of an equation, we are on somewhat safer scientific ground. The key things we need to look for are whether or not the coefficient estimates are statistically significant – individually through the t-ratios and jointly through the F-test. We also need to assess the goodness of fit of the equation through the *R*-squared and other related statistics. Finally, anticipating the discussion of later chapters, we need to examine the residuals of the model for any obvious signs of misspecification.

Examination of the equation in Figure 5.1 suggests a reasonable fit to the data. The coefficients appear to be significant and the overall fit is good (an *R*-squared of 0.5 for data in difference form is quite reasonable). However, the Durbin-Watson statistic should take a value of 2.0 if there is no serial correlation present and therefore a value of 0.61 is a warning sign that there may be statistical problems present which will need to be addressed. This will form the main theme of the next chapter.

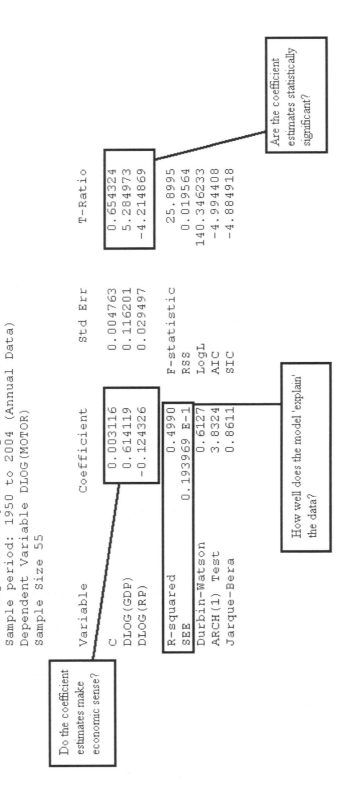

Figure 5.1: Interpreting Regression Output – A first look at the results

Exercises for Chapter 5

These exercises use the data in the workfile FM.IRG. This contains annual data for the US economy over the period 1959 to 2007. The data are taken from the Federal Reserve Board of St. Louis database (FRED). The expenditure variables are all in constant prices.

Exercise 1

The following regression results were obtained by regressing the change in consumption (DC) on the change in autonomous expenditures (DA) and the change in real money balances (DRM). Autonomous expenditures are defined as the sum of investment, government consumption and exports. Real money balances consist of broad money (M2) deflated by the consumer price index (P).

```
Ordinary Least Squares Regression Results
Sample period: 1960 to 2007 (Annual Data)
Dependent Variable DC
Sample Size 48
```

Variable	Coefficient	Std Err	T-Ratio
C	50.841678	10.059046	5.054323
DA	0.571294	0.067305	8.488065
DRM	39.294565	6.249613	6.287519
R-squared	0.7341		
SEE	41.676845		

a) Comment on the coefficient estimates. How can these be interpreted sensibly?

b) Using the information in the table calculate (i) the residual sum of squares and (ii) the F statistic for this regression.

c) Perform an F-test for the joint significance of the two variables on the right hand side of the equation using a 5% level of significance.

Exercise 2. The following sample moments are calculated using the same data set:

```
Sample period: 1960 to 2007 (Annual Data)

Sample Moments

Variable              DC                DA                DRM
Mean             139.545833         87.281250          0.988454
Standard Dev      79.088722         90.831278          0.978213
```

a) Using these sample moments, calculate estimates of the elasticity of consumption expenditure with respect to autonomous expenditures and with respect to real money balances.

b) Re-estimate the original equation but this time use percentage changes in consumption, autonomous expenditures and real money balances as the equation variables. Compare the coefficient estimates with the elasticities you estimated in part (d) and comment.

Exercise 3.

Using the data in the workfile estimate an equation which allows for separate effects of the different components of autonomous expenditures i.e.

$$DC_t = \beta_1 + \beta_2 DI_t + \beta_3 DG_t + \beta_4 DX_t + \beta_5 DRM_t + u_t$$

where I, G and X are investment, government spending and exports respectively.

a) Examine the coefficients of your estimated model and assess which categories of autonomous expenditure have the most important effect on consumption expenditures.

b) Perform an F-test for the hypothesis that the coefficients on the three categories of autonomous expenditure are equal.

Chapter 6: Serial Correlation

6.1 Introduction

One of the most important assumptions of the classical linear regression model is that the errors in the regression relationship should be independent of each other. The reason why we make this assumption is that it allows us to determine the statistical distribution of the parameter estimates. This in turn allows us to perform hypothesis tests and to derive confidence intervals for the coefficients of our model. Unfortunately, this assumption can fail in a variety of situations and is particularly problematic when we are working with time series data.

A data series is classified as a time series when it consists of observations of a random variable X made at different points in time. For example, the Office of National Statistics website allows us to download estimates of Gross Domestic Product on an annual basis over the period 1955 to the present. From a statistical point of view however, such a data series cannot be treated as a random sample. If a sample of data is truly random then it can be re-ordered or 'shuffled' without loss of information. In the case of a time series however, the ordering of the data contains important information. We can see this by simply plotting a data series like GDP. This will show a generally increasing trend, albeit with some random variation around the trend path. In other words, the level of GDP in one year is not independent of the level of GDP in the previous year.

Now consider a regression model of the form $Y_t = \alpha + \beta X_t + u_t$ where Y and X are time series variables. Given the nature of the data, it is highly likely that u, the error term in this relationship, will also behave like a time series variable in the sense that it will depend upon its own past values. In such circumstances, we say that there is *serial correlation* in the errors and therefore, because the errors are not independent of each other, we cannot assume that the distributional results we have derived under the assumption of independent errors are reliable.

Serial correlation of the errors is a serious problem when dealing with time series data. In this chapter we will discuss how econometricians deal with this problem. There are three basic stages to this.

Consequences: First we discuss the implications of serial correlation for least squares regression. We concentrate on the first two moments of the distribution of the least squares regression estimates and show that serial correlation does not, in itself, mean that the least squares estimates will exhibit bias, although it will mean that the standard formulas for the variances of the least squares coefficients will typically produced biased estimates.

Detection: Next we must decide if serial correlation is present and what specific form it takes. This involves the construction of statistical tests for the presence of serially correlated errors and diagnostic tools which allow us to determine which of a range of possible types of serial correlation best describes the errors of our particular model.

*Dealing with the pr*oblem: Finally, we consider what to do if serial correlation is present. Although mechanical 'corrections' are available to 'deal' with the problem, we will argue that these are usually not the correct way forward. Serial correlation is often a symptom of a deeper problem with the estimated model and a better strategy is usually to consider how we can design models which avoid the problem in the first place.

6.2 Causes of serial correlation

Consider a regression equation of the standard form:

$$Y_t = \beta X_t + u_t \tag{6.1}$$

The errors of this model are said to be serially correlated if $E\left(u_t u_{t-k}\right) \neq 0$ for some $k \neq 0$. Why might serial correlation arise? The simplest assumption we can make is that it arises because of some intrinsic property of the errors. For example, because of the time series nature of the data, we might assume that shocks to the equation are not random drawings from a particular distribution but instead depend upon their own past values. For example, the error in each time period may depend explicitly on the error in the previous time period giving rise to a *first-order autoregressive process*. This would mean that the error process could be described by a second equation of the form $u_t = \rho u_{t-1} + \varepsilon_t$ where ε is a truly random disturbance and $\rho \neq 0$. However, this is not the only form of serial correlation which can occur. An alternative is where the error term in the equation is an average over several time periods of the truly random disturbance ε. For example, we might have a *first-order moving average process* of the form $u_t = \varepsilon_t + \lambda \varepsilon_{t-1}$. Both of these error processes are said to be serially correlated but each produces different implications and problems for the modeller. However, in both cases the problem of dealing with serial correlation is simplified because of the assumption that it is an intrinsic feature of the error themselves, i.e. that the problem is one of *error dynamics*. A more realistic conclusion might be that the errors are serially correlated because of some fundamental misspecification in the original equation (6.1).

The assumption of error dynamics is very convenient because it makes the serial problem entirely statistical. If this is assumption is true then the basic equation is correctly specified and all we need to worry about is 'dealing' with the serial correlation in the errors. The presence of serial correlation in the errors does mean that ordinary least squares will not be an efficient estimator and will have a number of other undesirable properties. However, these are essentially statistical problems which can be dealt with through mechanical procedures such as the adjustment of the OLS estimator or the use of alternative estimators. The problem with this approach is that, if the serial correlation is the result of some other problem with the model, then we may end up disguising this problem and therefore making unjustified claims for the accuracy of our original equation.

To illustrate how serial correlation can arise as the result of a misspecified model consider the case of *omitted variables*. Suppose the true regression model takes the form:

$$Y_t = \beta_1 X_{t1} + \beta_2 X_{t2} + u_t \tag{6.2}$$

but we estimate a model of the form:

$$Y_t = \beta_1 X_{t1} + \omega_t \tag{6.3}$$

If follows that the error from (6.3) is determined partly by the error from the true model and partly by the effects of the omitted variable. That is, we have $\omega_t = u_t + \beta_2 X_{t2}$. Now, if the X_2 variable is itself serially correlated, which is very often the case with economic data, then the effect of omitting this variable is to introduce serial correlation into the errors of the misspecified model.

A more subtle form of the omitted variable problem is that of *dynamic misspecification*. This arises when the regression model contains the correct variables are present but the true model allows for dynamic adjustment processes which are not present in the regression specification. Dynamic misspecification can arise for a variety of reasons. For example, consider the following model:

$$Y_t^* = \beta X_t + u_t \tag{6.4}$$
$$\Delta Y_t = \gamma \left(Y_t^* - Y_{t-1} \right) \tag{6.5}$$

The first equation (6.4) specifies the determination of an equilibrium or desired value of Y while the second (6.5) describes how the actual value of Y adjusts towards that desired value. Combining equations (6.4) and (6.5) yields the following model:

$$Y_t = \beta \gamma X_t + \left(1 - \gamma \right) Y_{t-1} + \gamma u_t \tag{6.6}$$

This is the standard *partial adjustment* model which has featured heavily in applied econometric research. From (6.6) it is clear that a simple regression of Y on X will be misspecified since it omits the lagged Y term. Moreover, since it is highly likely that Y will be serially correlated, it follows that a simple regression is likely to suffer from serial correlation in the errors.

6.3 Consequences of serial correlation

Now that we have established some of the reasons why serial correlation may arise in regression models, let us consider the implications for least squares regression analysis. Suppose we have a model in which the errors follow a first-order autoregressive process as set out in (6.7):

$$Y_t = \beta X_t + u_t$$
$$u_t = \rho u_{t-1} + \varepsilon_t \tag{6.7}$$

where ε is a vector of independent, identically distributed random disturbances with mean zero and constant variance. As we have seen this is not the only possible type of serial correlation which may arise but it is sufficiently general (and sufficiently common in practice) to be of use in discussing the consequences of serial correlation.

One of the useful features of the autoregressive process defined in (6.7) is that it can be written in moving average form. Using backward substitution we have:

$$u_t = \varepsilon_t + \rho \varepsilon_{t-1} + \rho^2 \varepsilon_{t-2} \ldots = \sum_{j=0}^{\infty} \rho^j \varepsilon_{t-j} \tag{6.8}$$

This is an *infinite moving average* process. Providing $|\rho| < 1$ then the sequence defined in (6.8) will converge in the sense that it will have a finite variance. To see this note that

$E\left(u_t^2\right) = \sum_{j=0}^{\infty} \rho^{2j} E\left(\varepsilon_{t-j}^2\right) = \sum_{j=0}^{\infty} \rho^{2j} \sigma_\varepsilon^2 = \dfrac{\sigma_\varepsilon^2}{1-\rho^2}$, therefore we need $|\rho| < 1$ for the variance of the error term to be finite and positive. If $|\rho| < 1$ then the process is said to be *weakly stationary* and it can be shown that a general feature of stationary, finite autoregressive processes is that they can be written as infinite moving average processes. Moreover, since $E(\varepsilon_{t-j}) = 0; \forall j$ it follows that $E(u_t) = 0$. This is a useful property since we have already seen that the expected value of the OLS estimator can be written as $E(\hat{\beta}) = \beta + \sum_{t=1}^{T} x_t E(u_t) / \sum_{t=1}^{T} x_t^2$. It therefore follows that $E(\hat{\beta}) = \beta$ and that the OLS estimator is unbiased even when the errors are serially correlated.

The result we have just derived can be stated as follows. The presence of serial correlation does not *in itself* indicate that the OLS estimator is unbiased . The phrase 'in itself' needs to be emphasised, since the unbiasedness of the OLS estimator has really only be demonstrated in the case where the serial correlation is due to pure error dynamics. More generally, if serial correlation is a symptom of some other misspecification, then we cannot rely on OLS remaining unbiased. For example, suppose we had omitted a serially correlated variable X_2 from the model which should have been present, then it is straightforward to show that the OLS estimator will be biased.

The other important point to note is that, even if the OLS estimator is unbiased, it will be inefficient. This follows from the fact that efficiency of the OLS estimator depends on the all the Gauss-Markov assumptions holding. If the assumption of serially independent errors fails then we can, in principle, design a more efficient estimator which takes into account this property. Therefore, in models with serially correlated errors, it is always possible in principle to design an estimator with a lower variance than the OLS estimator.

Perhaps the most serious implication of serial correlation is that the OLS estimator of the standard error of the coefficient estimate(s) will be biased. From our earlier treatment of the OLS estimator, we have:

$$V\left(\hat{\beta}\right)=E\left(\hat{\beta}-E\left(\hat{\beta}\right)\right)^2=E\left(\hat{\beta}-\beta\right)^2=E\left(\frac{\sum X_t u_t}{\sum X_t^2}\right)^2 \qquad (6.9)$$

In that earlier treatment we made use of the Gauss-Markov assumption that $E\left(u_t u_{t-k}\right)=0; \forall k \neq 0$. This allowed us to eliminate all the cross-product terms from the summation in order to arrive at the result that $V\left(\hat{\beta}\right)=\sigma_u^2 / \sum x_t^2$. Unfortunately, we can no longer make this simplification when the errors are serially correlated. If we make a further assumption that the X variable is itself follows an AR(1) process of the form $X_t=\phi X_{t-1}+v_t$ then it is possible (with some straightforward but tedious algebra) to show that the variance of the OLS estimator for β can be written:

$$V\left(\hat{\beta}\right)=\frac{\sigma_u^2}{\sum X_t^2}\left(1+2\rho\phi+2\rho^2\phi^2+2\rho^3\phi^3......\right)=\frac{\sigma_u^2}{\sum X_t^2}\left(\frac{1+\rho\phi}{1-\rho\phi}\right) \qquad (6.10)$$

Examination of (6.10) shows that, if ρ and ϕ are both positive and less than one (reasonable assumptions for many economic models), then the true variance of the OLS estimator will be larger than the estimated variance. Moreover, the closer ρ and ϕ are to one, then the larger will be the bias.

Example: To illustrate the implications of serial correlation we have described, 1,000 regressions were run using artificially generated data for the model given below:

$$\begin{aligned}Y_t &= X_t + u_t \\ X_t &= 0.9X_{t-1} + \varepsilon_{t1} \\ u_t &= 0.9u_{t-1} + \varepsilon_{t2}\end{aligned} \qquad (6.11)$$

where ε_1 and ε_2 are independent white-noise errors.

A typical regression taken from this simulation looks like this:

$$\hat{Y}_t = -2.3872 + 0.7603\, X_t$$
$$(0.27) \quad (0.12)$$

$$R^2 = 0.31 \qquad \hat{\sigma} = 2.22 \qquad T = 100 \tag{6.12}$$

The test statistic for the null hypothesis that the slope coefficient is equal to one is $t = (0.7603 - 1)/0.12 = -2.0$ and under the null hypothesis this is distributed as t_{98}. Since the 5% critical value for a two-tailed test is +/- 1.96, we therefore reject the null at the 5% level. This result is by no means unusual for this simulation. Out of 1,000 regressions we reject the null that the slope coefficient is equal to one in 514 cases.

The reason why we reject the null so often is not because of any bias in the coefficient estimates. The distribution of the slope coefficient estimates from our simulation is illustrated in the histogram shown in Figure 6.1:

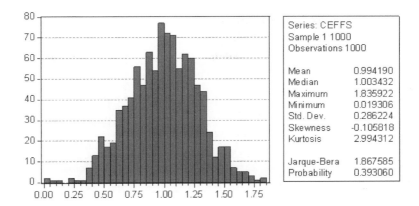

Figure 6.1: Distribution of slope coefficients from Monte Carlo simulation of a model with an AR(1) error

The average slope coefficient estimate is 0.9942 which is very close to the true value of one. Instead, the reason lies in the underestimate of the standard error of the slope coefficient which has resulted from the fact that both the errors and the X variable are serially correlated. To see this compare the standard error of the slope coefficient from the regression equation (6.12) with the standard error of the slope coefficients from the simulation exercise shown in Figure 6.1. The latter provides an unbiased estimate of the standard error and, if we had used this to calculate our test statistic, we would not have rejected the null.

6.4 Detection of serial correlation

In our discussion of tests for serial correlation it will be helpful to have a particular example in mind. Consider the following estimated consumption function for the UK economy based on annual data from 1955 to 2001.

$$
\ln\left(C_t\right) = 8.9916 + 0.9569 \ln\left(YD_t\right) + \hat{u}_t
$$
$$
 (0.04) \quad (0.011)
$$
$$
R^2 = 0.99 \qquad \hat{\sigma} = 0.0273 \qquad T = 47
$$

(6.13)

123

C is total consumers' expenditure and *YD* is real personal disposable income. Both variables are measured in millions of pounds at 1995 prices.

On first inspection this equation appears to have reasonable properties. The slope coefficient measures the income elasticity of consumption expenditure and a value close to one is therefore economically reasonable. The slope coefficient is statistically significantly different from zero and the coefficient of determination indicates a good fit. One point to note is that the slope coefficient is significantly less than one at the 5% level with a t-statistic for the null that this coefficient is equal to one taking a value of $(0.9569-1)/0.11$ $=-3.92$. However, we have already seen that serial correlation can lead to an underestimate of the standard errors of the regression coefficients and, therefore, this result may be misleading. Therefore, in order to assess how robust are our estimates of the model's parameters, we need to test for the presence of serial correlation in the residuals $\hat{u}$ from equation (6.13).

6.4.1 Informal 'tests' for serial correlation

We can look for serial correlation informally by simply inspecting a plot of the residuals. If runs of positive or negative residuals are obvious then this is a sign that serial correlation is present. For example, Figure 6.2 shows the residuals for our consumption function equation and it is obvious that there are periods during which the residuals are consistently either positive or negative. This is a clear indication that the equation suffers from serial correlation. However, the problem with an informal procedure like this is that it tells us little about the form that this serial correlation might take. Moreover, visual inspection of the residuals may fail to detect some forms of serial correlation such as moving average errors. Therefore, it is important to develop more formal tests as well as procedures for identifying the specific form of serial correlation which is relevant for this equation.

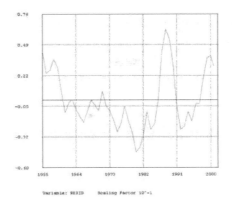

Figure 6.2: Residuals for equation (6.13)

The *correlogram* provides another method for the investigation of serial correlation. This consists of a sequence of autocorrelations of the residuals with their own past values. We can define the sample correlogram as:

$$\hat{\rho}_k = \sum_{t=k+1}^{T} \hat{u}_t \hat{u}_{t-k} \Big/ \sum_{t=1}^{T} \hat{u}_t^2 \qquad (6.14)$$

The sample autocorrelations are constrained to lie on the interval $]-1,1[$ for $k \neq 0$. Experienced modellers can identify the nature of the serial correlation process by inspection of the sample correlogram. For example, the correlogram of the residuals from our consumption function is given in Figure 6.3. The pattern of autocorrelations shows an initial positive value which declines quickly towards zero and then cycles around zero. This is indicative of a second order autocorrelation process with complex roots.

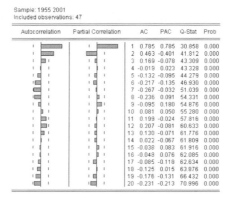

Sample: 1955 2001
Included observations: 47

Autocorrelation	Partial Correlation		AC	PAC	Q-Stat	Prob
		1	0.785	0.785	30.858	0.000
		2	0.463	-0.401	41.812	0.000
		3	0.169	-0.078	43.309	0.000
		4	-0.019	0.023	43.328	0.000
		5	-0.132	-0.095	44.279	0.000
		6	-0.217	-0.135	46.930	0.000
		7	-0.267	-0.032	51.039	0.000
		8	-0.236	0.091	54.331	0.000
		9	-0.095	0.180	54.876	0.000
		10	0.081	0.050	55.280	0.000
		11	0.199	-0.024	57.816	0.000
		12	0.207	-0.081	60.633	0.000
		13	0.130	-0.071	61.776	0.000
		14	0.022	-0.067	61.809	0.000
		15	-0.038	0.083	61.916	0.000
		16	-0.048	0.076	62.085	0.000
		17	-0.085	-0.118	62.634	0.000
		18	-0.125	0.015	63.876	0.000
		19	-0.176	-0.131	66.432	0.000
		20	-0.231	-0.213	70.996	0.000

Figure 6.3: Correlogram of residuals from equation (6.13)

The *partial autocorrelations* allow for the presence of intermediate lags in the autoregressive process. In this case, for example, we see that both the first and the second order partial autocorrelations lie outside the standard error bands. This indicates a second order autoregressive process.

6.4.2 Formal tests for serial correlation

The first formal test for serial correlation which we will discuss is the *Durbin-Watson* test. This is a standard part of the regression output for most econometrics packages. It tests for a specific form of serial correlation i.e. first order autocorrelation but is arguably sensitive to other forms also.

Consider the following regression model with an error which follows an autoregressive process of order one:

$$Y_t = \beta X_t + u_t$$
$$u_t = \rho u_{t-1} + \varepsilon_t \tag{6.15}$$

Taking the residuals from an OLS regression of Y on X, we can construct the test statistic:

$$DW = \sum_{t=2}^{T} (\hat{u}_t - \hat{u}_{t-1})^2 / \sum_{t=1}^{T} \hat{u}_t^2 \qquad (6.16)$$

DW can be seen as a test for the null hypothesis that $\rho = 0$ in (6.15). To see this, expand the numerator of (6.16) to obtain:

$$DW = \frac{\sum_{t=2}^{T} \hat{u}_t^2 + \sum_{t=2}^{T} \hat{u}_{t-1}^2 - 2\sum_{t=2}^{T} \hat{u}_t \hat{u}_{t-1}}{\sum_{t=1}^{T} \hat{u}_t^2} \qquad (6.17)$$

Now for large T we have $\sum_{t=2}^{T} \hat{u}_t^2 \approx \sum_{t=2}^{T} \hat{u}_{t-1}^2 \approx \sum_{t=1}^{T} \hat{u}_t^2$ and $\sum_{t=2}^{T} \hat{u}_t \hat{u}_{t-1} / \sum_{t=1}^{T} \hat{u}_t^2 \approx \hat{\rho}$ where $\hat{\rho}$ is the first autocorrelation of the least squares residuals. It follows that $DW \approx 2(1 - \hat{\rho})$. Therefore if there is no autocorrelation then $E(DW) = 2$, if there is positive autocorrelation ($\rho > 0$), then $E(DW) < 2$ and, if there is negative autocorrelation ($\rho < 0$), then $E(DW) > 2$. Note that the DW statistic is bounded between 0 and 4.

In order to use the Durbin-Watson statistic to conduct a test for autocorrelation, we need appropriate critical values. Unfortunately, there is a problem here in that the distribution of this statistic does not allow a simple accept/reject decision in the way we are used to. Instead, the distribution gives us upper and lower bounds for the test statistic under the null. For example, consider the case in which we wish to test $H_0 : \rho = 0$ against the alternative $H_1 : \rho > 0$. That is we wish to test the null that there is no autocorrelation against the alternative that there is positive first-order autocorrelation. From the Durbin-Watson tables we find that the upper and lower bounds at the 5% level are $d_U = 1.57$ and $d_U = 1.44$ respectively (note that these critical values are for a one-tailed test since the test specified has a one-sided alternative). If the test statistic is greater than d_U then we can accept the null, if it less than d_L then we reject the null but if $d_L < DW < d_U$ then we are in a region of indeterminacy which allows us to neither accept nor reject the null. If the DW statistic is greater than 2 then the relevant upper and lower critical values become $4 - d_U$ and $4 - d_L$. Thus the decision part of the testing procedure becomes rather more complicated than is usually the case. With this in mind, Figure 6.4 summarises the possible situations that can arise when conducting the Durbin-Watson test.

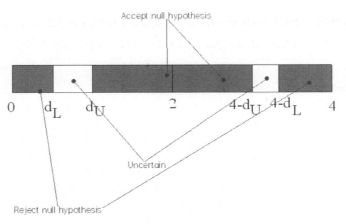

Figure 6.4: Possible decisions with the Durbin-Watson test

In the case of our consumption function we note that the DW statistic is 0.34. Since this is less than two we conclude that any first-order autocorrelation will be positive in nature. Secondly, since $DW < d_L$ we conclude that there is evidence of significant first order autocorrelation at the 5% level. However, it should also be noted that the pattern of autocorrelations shown in Figure 6.2 indicated a different type of serial correlation (second-order rather than first-order) and, on that basis, it may be that the Durbin-Watson test is not sufficiently general in this case.

A more general test for serial correlation is the *Q-statistic* which is shown in Figure 6.3. This is also known as the *Box-Ljung* test statistic for autocorrelation and tests for autocorrelation up to order J. The test statistic is defined as:

$$Q = T(T+2) \sum_{j=1}^{J} \frac{\hat{\rho}_j^2}{T-J} \qquad (6.18)$$

This test statistic is distributed as χ_2^J under the null that $\rho_j = 0; j = 1,..,J$. Note that this test can have low power when a large value of J is chosen since the inclusion of low values of $\hat{\rho}_j$ for large values of j can to some extent offset significant values for low j.

Another test for serial correlation is the *Breusch-Godfrey* test. This derives from a two stage testing procedure in which the residuals from a simple regression are regressed on the original variables plus their own lags. An F-test or a Chi-squared test is then used to test for the joint significance of the lags in this second-stage regression. For example, if we take the residuals from (6.13) then we can perform a second stage regression of the form:

$$\hat{u}_t = 0.0038 - 0.0010 \ln(YD_t) + 1.2314 \hat{u}_{t-1} - 0.5542 \hat{u}_{t-2} + v_t$$
$$\quad (0.02) \quad (0.006) \qquad\qquad (0.13) \qquad\qquad (0.13) \qquad\qquad\qquad (6.19)$$

$$F = 38.69 \qquad TR^2 = 33.26$$

Under the null hypothesis that there is no serial correlation, the F statistic is distributed as $F_{2.43}$ while TR^2 is distributed as χ_2^2. The 5% critical value for the F distribution with $(2,43)$ degrees of freedom is 3.21 and the 5% critical value for χ_2^2 is 5.99. Therefore, using either test, we reject the null that there is no serial correlation in the residuals.

Example: Structural Breaks and Serial Correlation

Although we often think of serial correlation as deriving principally from dynamic misspecification, there are a number of other ways in which it can arise. For example, suppose we have a structural break in the data series. An example of this is given in the diagram below. The series shown in the graph is artificially generated using the formula:

$$Y_t = \begin{cases} 0.5t + u_t & t = 1, \ldots, 50 \\ 5 + 0.5t + u_t & t = 51, \ldots, 100 \end{cases}$$

where u_t are iid normal random variables. Thus this series is constructed to have a structural break at observation 51 but there is no serial correlation in the errors.

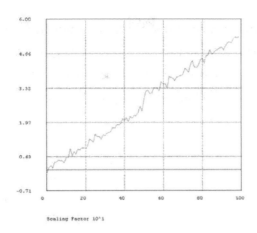

Figure 6.5: Simulation of a variable with a deterministic trend and a structural break

Now if we regress y on a constant and a time-trend, then we obtain the following equation:

```
Ordinary Least Squares Regression Results
Sample period: 1 to 100 (Annual Data)
Dependent Variable Y
Sample Size 100

Variable            Coefficient         Std Err        T-Ratio

C                     -1.767679        0.329669      -5.361979
TREND                  0.574179     5.667547 E-3     101.309984

R-squared               0.9905        F-statistic   10263.7129
SEE                   1.635998        RSS             262.296072
Durbin-Watson         0.8837          LogL           -190.109040
ARCH(1) Test          7.8652          AIC               3.842181
Jarque-Bera           2.9381          SIC               3.894284

Autocorrelations

                    AR Coeff            Q-stat      5% crit val

Order 1               0.5552          31.7569          3.841
Order 2               0.4649          54.2478          5.991
Order 3               0.3934          70.5190          7.815
Order 4               0.4998          97.0627          9.488
```

These results give every indication of the presence of serial correlation. The Durbin-Watson statistic of 0.88 lies below the lower bound of 1.5 and the Q or Box-Ljung statistics all indicate significant serial correlation in the regression residuals. However, this has arisen because of the structural break in the series itself rather than any property of the equation errors. What has happened is that the regression equation we have estimated has effectively

131

averaged out the two regimes. It therefore tends to overpredict Y in the first regime and underpredict Y in the second regime. Thus we tend to observe consistent runs first negative and then positive residuals. This illustrates the danger of mechanical corrections for serial correlation. For example, suppose we re-estimate our model allowing for an AR(1) error. This yields the following results:

```
Autoregressive Least Squares Results
Dependent Variable Y
Sample period: 3 to 100 (Annual Data)
Sample Size 99
Date Jan 07, 2010

Variable          Coefficient        Std Err        T-Ratio

Intercept          -1.791204            -              -
TREND               0.574706         0.011055       51.982258
AR1                 0.560082         0.082404        6.796759

R-squared             0.9982         SEE             1.364693
RSS               178.789201         DW              2.2742

Root of AR polynomial          0.5600

Converged on iteration 180
```

This may appear to have dealt with the problem in that the Durbin-Watson statistic for the residuals from this equation are much close to 2. However, it has done nothing to tackle the real cause of the problem which is the structural break half-way through the sample period. This example also illustrates a general problem in that it shows that diagnostic tests such as the Durbin-Watson test may fail due to causes other than that for which the test is designed. Rejection of the null hypothesis when testing for serial correlation certainly indicates a problem with the model. However, there are numerous different underlying problems which may give rise to such a result.

6.5 Dealing with serial correlation

One method of dealing with serial correlation is to jointly estimate the parameters of the equation under consideration and those which describe the behaviour of the error term. For example, consider the case in which we have an AR(2) error process, the model we wish to estimate can be written as:

$$Y_t = \beta X_t + u_t$$
$$u_t = \rho_1 u_{t-1} + \rho_2 u_{t-2} + \varepsilon_t$$

(6.20)

This can be written in the form shown in equation (6.21):

$$Y_t = \beta x_t - \rho_1 \beta X_{t-1} - \rho_2 \beta X_{t-2} + \rho_1 Y_{t-1} + \rho_2 Y_{t-2} + \varepsilon_t$$

(6.21)

This can then be estimated by a variety of different methods. Taking our consumption function (6.13) and allowing for an AR(2) error process yields the following parameter estimates.

```
Autoregressive Least Squares Results
Dependent Variable LC
Sample period: 1957 to 2001 (Annual Data)
Sample Size 45
Estimated using Cochrane-Orcutt method

Variable          Coefficient       Std Err          T-Ratio

Intercept          9.044978            -                -
LYD                0.943014         0.015409         61.198468
AR1                1.222045         0.135394          9.025842
AR2               -0.520208         0.137719         -3.777289

R-squared          0.9999          SEE              0.013481
RSS                0.007087        Durbin's h         1.3380
Durbin-Watson      1.8450

Roots of AR polynomial are complex

Real part = 0.6110     Complex part = 0.3832

Converged on iteration 12
```

Table 6.1: Estimates of consumption function with AR(2) error.

If we compare these results to the OLS estimates in equation (6.13), then we see that the estimate of the income elasticity of consumption has changed little. However, the standard error for this coefficient has increased noticeably from 0.011 to 0.015. This is due to the effect of serially correlated errors in producing a downward bias in the standard error of the OLS estimate. Since there is no evidence of serial correlation from the estimates in Table 6.1, we should treat the standard errors for the coefficient estimates of this equation as being much more reliable than the OLS estimates. Note however, that a test for the null hypothesis that the income elasticity is equal to one yields a test statistic $t = (0.943 - 1) / 0.0154 = -3.7$ and therefore we still reject this null hypothesis at the 5% significance level.

Another feature of note from Table 6.1 is that the roots of the autoregressive process for the residuals are complex. The residuals from this equation are modelled as a second order difference equation with a random error i.e.

$$\hat{u}_t = 1.2220 \, \hat{u}_{t-1} - 0.5202 \, \hat{u}_{t-2} + \varepsilon_t \qquad (6.22)$$

Now consider the characteristic roots of this equation which can be derived from the following quadratic equation $\lambda^2 - 1.2220\lambda + 0.5202 = 0$. This gives solutions $\lambda_{1,2} = 0.611 \pm 0.383\sqrt{-1}$. It is the presence of complex roots in this process which leads to the cycles in the correlogram which we observed in Figure 6.2. Although cycles in the correlogram are often associated with second order autoregressive processes, we should note that not all such processes produce cycles. Note that it is the presence of complex roots which is crucial. It is also possible to have an AR(2) process with real roots which does not produce cycles in the correlogram.

Time series analysts often difference series as a way of removing trends. However, this can sometimes produce serial correlation in cases where none is originally present. For example consider the following artificially generated example. The data are generated by the following equations:

$$X_t = 0.5t + u_{t1}$$
$$Y_t = 0.5X_t + 0.5t + u_{t2}$$

where u_1 and u_2 are independent iid normal random variables.

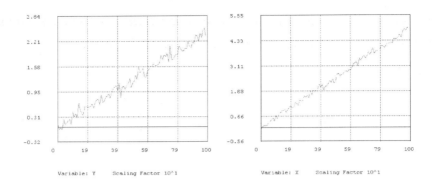

Variable: Y   Scaling Factor 10^1   Variable: X   Scaling Factor 10^1

Figure 6.6: Artificially generated trended series

Given the obvious trends in the series, it is tempting to difference them before estimation. If we do so then we obtain the following regression results:

```
Ordinary Least Squares Regression Results
Sample period: 2 to 100
Dependent Variable D(Y)
Sample Size 99

Variable          Coefficient       Std Err        T-Ratio

C                  -0.008438       0.142919       -0.059047
D(X)                0.470701       0.095455        4.931085

R-squared             0.2004    F-statistic       24.3156
SEE                 1.336158    RSS              173.175898
Durbin-Watson       3.0665      LogL            -168.154720
ARCH(1) Test        5.1188      AIC                3.437469
Jarque-Bera         2.0327      SIC                3.489896

Autocorrelations

                  AR Coeff       Q-stat      5% crit val
Order 1            -0.5515       31.0343          3.841
Order 2             0.1242       32.6247          5.991
Order 3            -0.1480       34.9069          7.815
Order 4             0.1396       36.9592          9.488
```

These look quite reasonable except for the fact that the Durbin-Watson statistic and the Q-statistics both indicate the presence of significant *negative* serial correlation despite the fact that the errors in our original model were not serially correlated. What has happened? The answer is that we have introduced a moving average error through the process of differencing. We can see this by differencing the equation for Y to obtain:

$$\Delta Y_t = 0.5 X_t + 0.5t + u_t - 0.5 X_{t-1} - 0.5(t-1) - u_{t-1}$$
$$= 0.5 \Delta X_t + 0.5 + u_t - u_{t-1}$$

This means that the error term in our differenced equation follows a first-order moving average process of the form $v_t = u_t + \alpha u_{t-1}$ with $\alpha = -1$. A better solution would have been to estimate the model in levels but include a time-trend. This yields:

```
Ordinary Least Squares Regression Results
Sample period: 2 to 101
Dependent Variable Y
Sample Size 100
```

Variable	Coefficient	Std Err	T-Ratio
C	-0.780249	0.223040	-3.498255
X	0.437726	0.096995	4.512854
TREND	0.536193	0.049245	10.888269

R-squared	0.9979	F-statistic	23343.3427
SEE	1.012692	RSS	99.477936
Durbin-Watson	1.9977	LogL	-141.632138
ARCH(1) Test	1.4388	AIC	2.892643
Jarque-Bera	0.9323	SIC	2.970798

Autocorrelations

	AR Coeff	Q-stat	5% crit val
Order 1	-0.0108	0.0120	3.841
Order 2	0.1551	2.5164	5.991
Order 3	-0.0451	2.7307	7.815
Order 4	-0.0539	3.0392	9.488

Note that the estimates of the slope coefficients are close to those used to construct the data. Also in this case there is no evidence of any serial correlation in the residuals.

6.6 Serial correlation as a simplifying assumption

In the previous section we saw that a model with an autoregressive error could be written as a single equation using lags of both the independent and dependent variables. For example, equation (6.21) can be used to estimate a model with an autoregressive error of order 2. This result gives rise to an interesting interpretation of models with serially correlated errors which was originally set out by Hendry and Mizon (1978). Suppose we start with a model which includes unrestricted lags on the independent and dependent variables. Such an equation is referred to as a general *autoregressive distributed lag* model. For example, we might have an equation of the form:

$$Y_t = \beta_1 X_t + \beta_2 X_{t-1} + \beta_3 X_{t-2} + \beta_4 Y_{t-1} + \beta_5 Y_{t-2} + \varepsilon_t \tag{6.23}$$

Note that this has five free parameters in contrast with the model with an AR(2) error which has only three. Now, if we place the following restrictions on the parameters of (6.23) - $\beta_2 = -\beta_1\beta_4, \beta_3 = -\beta_1\beta_5$ - then we can write this equation as:

$$Y_t = \beta_1 X_t - \beta_1\beta_4 X_{t-1} - \beta_1\beta_5 X_{t-2} + \beta_4 Y_{t-1} + \beta_5 Y_{t-2} + \varepsilon_t \tag{6.24}$$

This, in turn can be written as:

$$\begin{aligned} Y_t &= \beta_1 X_t + u_t \\ u_t &= \beta_4 u_{t-1} + \beta_5 u_{t-2} + \varepsilon_t \end{aligned} \tag{6.25}$$

In other words, by placing appropriate restrictions on a general ARDL model we can write it as a model which has no lags but does have an autoregressive error.

Another way of looking at this transformation is to write (6.23) in terms of the lag operator L. This gives us an equivalent equation of the form:

$$Y_t = \beta_1 X_t + \beta_2 LX_t + \beta_3 L^2 X_t + \beta_4 LY_t + \beta_5 LY_t + \varepsilon_t \tag{6.26}$$

Imposing the restrictions $\beta_2 = -\beta_1\beta_4, \beta_3 = -\beta_1\beta_5$ along with some simple algebraic manipulation yields:

$$\left(1 - \beta_4 L - \beta_5 L^2\right)Y_t = \beta_1\left(1 - \beta_4 L - \beta_5 L^2\right)X_t + \varepsilon_t \tag{6.27}$$

The fact that the same lag polynomial $\left(1 - \beta_4 L - \beta_5 L^2\right)$ appears on both the left and right hand sides of equation (6.27) indicates the presence of *common factors* in the lags of y and x. It is the presence of these common factors which allows us to write the model as a combination of a static equation linking Y to X with an autoregressive error.

Hendry and Mizon use this framework to argue that the use of autoregressive errors in regression models amounts to the imposition of common factor restrictions. These are simplifying assumptions because they reduce the number of parameters to be estimated from five in the general model (6.23) to only three in the model with an AR(2) error (6.25). The model with an AR(2) error is therefore more *parsimonious*, that is it requires fewer parameter estimates than the unrestricted model. However, the move to (6.25) involves the imposition of restrictions which should be tested before they are imposed. This creates some problems since the restrictions involve non-linear relationships between the parameters and hence, tests for these restrictions have non standard distributions.

Exercises for Chapter 6

Exercise 1

An econometrician has estimated the following model which relates UK investment expenditure to GDP.

```
Ordinary Least Squares Regression Results
Sample period: 1948 to 2005 (Annual Data)
Dependent Variable I
Sample Size 58

Variable            Coefficient        Std Err        T-Ratio

C                 -2.404671 E+4     2301.773340     -10.447037
Y                     0.180970        0.003390      53.381312

R-squared             0.9807     F-statistic       2849.5645
SEE              6399.427100     RSS             2.293349 E+9
Durbin-Watson         0.2844     LogL             -589.590684
ARCH(1) Test         28.5666     AIC                20.399678
Jarque-Bera           2.3482     SIC                20.470728

Autocorrelations

                    AR Coeff        Q-stat      5% crit val

Order 1               0.8425        43.3401          3.841
Order 2               0.6317        68.1423          5.991
Order 3               0.4655        81.8537          7.815
Order 4               0.3118        88.1203          9.488
```

The residuals are shown in the graph:

a) The econometrician then claims that this is an excellent model because it has a high R^2 and the t-statistic for the slope coefficient is very large. Explain to him (firmly but politely!) why he is wrong.

b) Using the information given in the regression table, perform two tests for the presence of first order autocorrelation in the residuals.

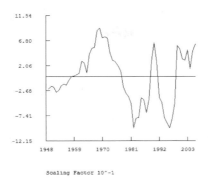

Scaling Factor 10^-1

Exercise 2

Following your explanation of his result, the econometrician is sufficiently worried about his model to perform a further test for autocorrelation. This involves running the following regression in which RESID are the regression residuals from the first regression.

```
Ordinary Least Squares Regression Results
Sample period: 1949 to 2005
Dependent Variable RESID
Sample Size 57
```

Variable	Coefficient	Std Err	T-Ratio
C	-398.625819	1237.530950	-0.322113
Y	0.000892	0.001810	0.492836
RESID(-1)	0.868168	0.071120	12.207001

R-squared	0.7340	F-statistic	74.5192
SEE	3354.365909	RSS	6.075956 E8
Durbin-Watson	1.4823	LogL	-542.065608
ARCH(1) Test	0.1000	AIC	19.125109
Jarque-Bera	27.9022	SIC	19.232638

a) Using the results from this table, calculate the Breusch-Godfrey test statistic for the presence of first order autocorrelation.

b) Set out the null and alternative hypotheses for the Breusch-Godfrey test, state the distribution for the test statistic under the null and perform the test by comparing the test statistic with the 5% critical value under the null.

Exercise 3

Using the data in workfile NAC.IRG estimate a model of the form:

$$\Delta I_t = \beta_1 + \beta_2 \Delta Y_t + u_t$$

a) Examine the residuals from this model. Is there any visual evidence of serial correlation?

b) Perform the Durbin-Watson, Ljung-Box and Breusch-Godfrey tests for first order autocorrelation. Do these tests produce the same result?

c) What does your analysis of the residuals of this model suggest about the properties of the OLS estimator? How does your answer differ from the conclusions you reached regarding the model estimated in question 1.

Chapter 7: Heteroscedasticity

7.1 Introduction

The presence of heteroscedasticity in the errors of a regression model is a failure of the third assumption of the Classical Linear Regression Model in that $E\left(u_i^2\right) \neq \sigma_u^2$ for all $i = 1,...,N$. In many ways the presence of heteroscedasticity creates problems similar to those found when serial correlation is present. For example, the presence of heteroscedasticity means that Ordinary Least Squares estimates become inefficient and, although its presence does not in itself mean that OLS estimates become unbiased, it makes statistical testing based on OLS estimates unreliable. Unlike the case of serial correlation, we will see that heteroscedasticity is most often a feature of econometric models based on cross-section (rather than time-series) data.

In this chapter we will investigate the causes and implications of heteroscedasticity in detail. We will begin by investigating situations in which the phenomenon can arise followed by a discussion of its consequences. This is followed by discussions of methods through which the presence of heteroscedasticity can be detected, how it can be dealt with and finally, a discussion of the autoregressive conditional heteroscedasticity (ARCH) model which has featured prominently in the financial econometrics literature in recent years.

7.2 Causes of heteroscedasticity

Consider a regression model of the standard form $Y_i = \beta X_i + u_i$. Heteroscedasticity is said to occur in any situation in which $E\left(u_i^2\right)$ varies with the value of i. Now, this is a very broad definition and it is therefore useful to consider some more specific cases which may arise in practice. One case which frequently arises is where the variance of the error term is a function of the exogenous variable $E\left(u_i^2\right) = f\left(X_i\right)$. This naturally arises in many cross-section regression models. For example, consider a model of consumption expenditures based on a cross-section of households. Although we would reasonably expect the level of consumption to vary with the level of income we might also reasonably expect the variability of consumption to also depend on income levels. A special case of this could be where the variance of the error term is proportional to the square of the exogenous variable which would generate a model of the form:

$$Y_i = \beta X_i + u_i$$
$$E\left(u_i^2\right) = \sigma_u^2 X_i^2 \tag{7.1}$$

Equation (7.1) is a particularly easy case to deal with because it suggests a natural re-scaling of the data which would eliminate heteroscedasticity. If divide both sides of (7.1) to rewrite the model as $Y_i / X_i = \beta + v_i$ where $v_i = u_i / X_i$, the heteroscedasticity is effectively eliminated. To see this, take expectations of the squared error term in the new form of the model to obtain $E\left(v_i^2\right) = E\left(u_i^2\right) / X_i^2 = \sigma_u^2$. This shows that the errors of the revised model have constant variance (i.e. are homoscedastic) and therefore that heteroscedasticity is no longer a problem.

Unfortunately there is no guarantee that the heteroscedasticity we encounter will be of the convenient form found in equation (7.1). More generally, we might find a relationship between the error variance and the exogenous variable of the form $E\left(u_i^2\right) = \sigma_u^2 X_i^h$. If such a relationship exists then we can still rescale the data by dividing through by $X_i^{h/2}$. This yields a relationship of the form:

$$\frac{Y_i}{X_i^{h/2}} = \frac{\beta}{X_i^{h/2}} + v_i \tag{7.2}$$

v_i now has the desired properties for OLS estimation since $E\left(v_i^2\right) = \sigma_u^2$ but this now leads to a potential complication in that the parameter h is likely to be itself unknown and must therefore be estimated.

7.3 Consequences of heteroscedasticity

Heteroscedasticity does not, in itself, imply that OLS estimation will lead to biased coefficient estimates. To demonstrate this we note that the OLS estimator can be written as:

$$\hat{\beta} = \frac{\sum X_i Y_i}{\sum X_i^2} = \frac{\sum X_i (\beta X_i + u_i)}{\sum X_i^2} = \beta + \frac{\sum X_i u_i}{\sum X_i^2} \qquad (7.3)$$

Taking expectations of (7.3) gives:

$$E(\hat{\beta}) = \beta + \frac{\sum X_i E(u_i)}{\sum X_i^2} \qquad (7.4)$$

and this in turn yields $E(\hat{\beta}) = \beta$ providing that $E(u_i) = 0$. Therefore, providing that we can maintain assumptions 1 and 4 of the CLRM, we can prove unbiasedness. Since, we have not had to invoke the assumption of homoscedastic errors, this assumption is not necessary for the proof and therefore we have demonstrated that heteroscedasticity is not *in itself* a reason to believe that OLS will produce biased estimates.

The demonstration that heteroscedasticity does not lead to biased estimates above parallels that in the previous chapter where we showed that serial correlation does not imply bias. However, a similar caveat applies in this case. As with serial correlation, heteroscedasticity may be the result of some other form of misspecification. For example, it may be the result of omitting a relevant variable from the model. If this is the case then OLS estimates will be biased. However, this bias is the result of omitting the variable *not* the heteroscedasticity which arises as a symptom of the underlying misspecification.

Although heteroscedasticity does not imply that OLS will be biased, it does imply that OLS will be inefficient. Consider the following model expressed in matrix form:

$$y = X\beta + u$$
$$E(uu') = \sigma_u^2 V \tag{7.5}$$

where V is a positive-definite matrix. By virtue of the assumption that V is positive-definite, it can be expressed as $V = LL'$ where L is a non-singular matrix. This model is very general since it can allow for both heteroscedasticity and serial correlation in the errors. As a result this framework is referred to as the *Generalised Least Squares Model*.

If we pre-multiply (7.5) by the matrix L^{-1} then we obtain a model of the form:

$$L^{-1}y = L^{-1}X\beta + L^{-1}u \tag{7.6}$$

Now consider the properties of the error term from this transformed model, we have:

$$E\left(L^{-1}uu'\left(L^{-1}\right)'\right) = \sigma_u^2 L^{-1}V\left(L^{-1}\right)' = \sigma_u^2 I \tag{7.7}$$

What this shows is that an appropriate transformation of the data can produce a model which satisfies the CLRM assumptions of serial independence and homoscedasticity in the errors. It follows that application of OLS to the transformed data will produce the best-linear-unbiased estimates of the parameters of interest. In particular, OLS estimates of the parameters of interest based on the transformed model will have lower variance than OLS estimates based on the original data. Therefore OLS estimates based on model (7.5) will be inefficient.

The generalised least squares (GLS) estimator appears an attractive methodology but it does suffer from the problem that the matrix V is typically unknown in practice. However, it is often enough to know that such a matrix exists in principle in order to develop the theoretical properties of the estimator. There are also empirical methods by which the parameters of the V matrix can be estimated along with the β parameters.

In addition to the problem of inefficiency we can also show that the use of OLS estimation in conjunction with heteroscedastic errors leads to problems for statistical inference in that the estimates of the standard errors of the regression parameters are biased. If the variance of the error term is positively correlated with the exogenous variable(s) then we can also show that these standard errors are biased downwards leading to incorrect size of tests based on t-ratios. The following example illustrates this problem. In this example we have conducted 1,000 simulations of model (7.1) with β set equal to 1. The model estimated takes the form $Y_i = \alpha + \beta X_i + u_i$. The distribution of the slope coefficient estimates obtained is illustrated by the following histogram:

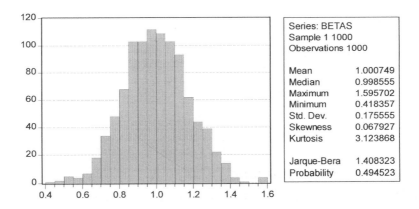

Series: BETAS	
Sample 1 1000	
Observations 1000	
Mean	1.000749
Median	0.998555
Maximum	1.595702
Minimum	0.418357
Std. Dev.	0.175555
Skewness	0.067927
Kurtosis	3.123868
Jarque-Bera	1.408323
Probability	0.494523

Figure 7.1: Distribution of coefficient estimates of model with heteroscedastic errors.

From the information given in Figure 7.1, we can see that the OLS estimator is not biased. The average coefficient estimate is extremely close to the true value of 1. However, out of the 1,000 regressions we estimate, the null hypothesis is rejected in 253 cases in favour of the two-sided alternative $H_1 : \beta \neq 1$ when 5% critical values for the *t*-test were used. If the test had the correct size then we should observe rejection about 50 cases for this simulation. The reason for this is that the standard error of the parameter estimate is typically underestimated. From Figure 7.1 we see that a reasonable estimate of this standard error is 0.17. However, the average estimate based on 1,000 simulations is 0.098.

Now consider a transformed model of the form $Y_i / X_i = \alpha / X_i + \beta + u_i / X_i$ in which the parameter of interest is the intercept β. We again ran 1,000 simulations of this model and obtained the histogram of OLS parameter estimates shown in Figure 7.2. This shows that the OLS estimator is again unbiased with an average value which is very close to the true value of one. The difference here is that estimates of the standard error of the parameter are now much more reliable. The average standard error from 1,000 regressions is 0.100 which is close to the standard error of the estimated coefficients of 0.099 shown in Figure 7.2. Moreover, we reject the null hypothesis $H_0 : \beta = 1$ in favour of the alternative $H_1 : \beta \neq 1$ only 49 times in this case. This is much closer to the 50 rejections predicted by the size of the test we have chosen.

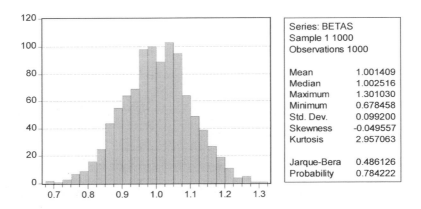

Figure 7.2: Coefficient estimates based on transformed model

7.4 Detection of heteroscedasticity

The easiest case to deal with when testing for heteroscedasticity is the case in which the variance of the error term is known to be related to a particular right-hand side variable. If this is the case, then it is easy to construct a formal test by examining the relationship between the squared regression residuals and the variable in question. What we would expect to see is that the spread of observations around the regression line should vary with the size of the exogenous variable. This is illustrated in Figure 7.3 below in which the variance of the residuals increases with the value of the exogenous variable X.

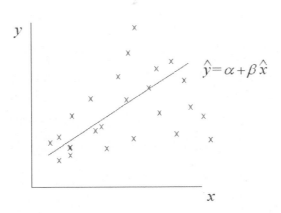

Figure 7.3 A regression model exhibiting heteroscedasticity

In cases like this the *Goldfeld-Quandt Test* provides a method of testing for the presence of heteroscedasticity. This is constructed as follows:

1. Order the data according to the size of the exogenous variable we believe is related to the variance of the error term.

2. Divide the sample into three sections of size $n, N-2n, n$ respectively. n should be approximately equal to $\frac{3}{8}N$.

3. Estimate separate regressions for the first and last n observations and generate the residual sum of squares. Then use the following F statistic $F = RSS_2 / RSS_1$ as the test statistic. Under the null hypothesis that the errors are homoscedastic this statistic will be distributed as $F_{n-k,n-k}$.

Note that our development of the Goldfeld-Quandt test has assumed that the variance increases with the size of the exogenous variable. It is also possible that the variance might decrease as x increases, in which case we would find $RSS_2 < RSS_1$. If this is the case then the appropriate test statistic would be $F = RSS_1 / RSS_2$.

Example: The following regression relates profits to numbers employed and capital stock employed for a sample of 472 large UK companies. Profits and capital are measured in £m and employment is measured as the number of workers employed. The data are taken from the *Financial Times 500* yearbook.

$$PR_i = -28.64 + \underset{(12.5)}{} \underset{(0.000617)}{0.004275} \ N_i + \underset{(0.00565)}{0.1199} \ K_i + \hat{u}_i$$

$$R^2 = 0.67 \qquad \hat{\sigma} = 229.7 \qquad F = 493.4 \qquad\qquad (7.8)$$

$$RSS = 24750928 \qquad i = 1, ..., 472$$

Equation (7.8) has reasonable statistical properties – both slope coefficients are statistically significant and the R^2 indicates that it 'explains' a large proportion of the variance of the endogenous variable. However, cross-section regressions of this type often exhibit heteroscedasticity. In order to detect whether this is the case we therefore apply the Goldfeld–Quandt test. To do this we first order the data according to the size of one of the right-hand side variables, here we will test for heteroscedasticity related to the size of the capital stock. We set $n = 3/8 \times 472 = 177$ and then estimate the model for two sub-samples – $i = 1, ..., 177$ and $i = 296, ..472$. Estimating separate regression equations for the two sub-samples yields $RSS_1 = 634685.8$ and $RSS_2 = 22581179$. The test statistics can therefore be calculated as:

$$F = \frac{RSS_2}{RSS_1} = \frac{22581179}{634685.8} = 355.8 \qquad\qquad (7.9)$$

Under the null hypothesis that the errors in this model are homoscedastic, this F statistic will follow the $F_{177,177}$ distribution. The 5% critical value for an F-distribution with 177 and

177 degrees of freedom is 1.28. Therefore we reject the null hypothesis at the 5% level and conclude that there is evidence of heteroscedasticity in this model.

One problem with the Goldfeld-Quandt test is that it requires an initial choice of which variable to use in ordering the data. In some situations there may be a natural choice but in others this may not be the case. The *White Test* provides a more flexible alternative which is based on the Lagrange multiplier testing principle. The idea here is that we use the residuals from the OLS regression model as the basis for a test of possible model misspecification. The White test can be constructed using the following procedure:

1. Estimate the model using OLS and generate the residuals.

2. Perform an auxiliary regression of the squared regression residuals on the levels and the squares of the right-hand side variables from the original model. If there are sufficient degrees of freedom then the cross-products of the regressors can also be included but in models with a large number of variables this may not be possible.

3. Perform either an *F*-test or a Chi-squared test for the joint significance of the right-hand side variables in the auxiliary regression.

For example, using the residuals from (7.8) we obtain the following auxiliary regression:

$$
\begin{aligned}
\hat{u}_i^2 = {}& - 24284 - 1.41\ N_i + 2.24\times10^{-5}\ N_i^2 - 1.25\times10^{-4}\ N_iK_i \\
& \ (16570)\ \ (1.62)\ \ \ \ \ (1.62\times10^{5})\ \ \ \ \ \ (1.9\times10^{4}) \\
& + 91.4\ K_i - 2.84\times10^{-3}\ K_i^2 + \hat{\varepsilon}_i \\
& \ (13.4)\ \ \ \ \ (8.4\times10^{4}) \\
& R^2 = 0.18 \qquad F = 21.13 \qquad N = 472
\end{aligned}
\tag{7.10}
$$

There are now two possible test statistics we can calculate using this auxiliary regression. The first is a Chi-squared test based on the statistic $NR^2 = 0.18\times472 = 84.96$. Under the null hypothesis that there is no heteroscedasticity then this statistic is distributed as χ_5^2

where the degrees of freedom is determined by the number of variables on the right-hand side of (7.10). The 5% critical value for the χ^2_5 distribution is 11.07, therefore we reject the null hypothesis in this case. Strictly, the White test is an asymptotic or large sample test and therefore the Chi-squared version is the more appropriate. However, some researchers have found that the F test, which is a finite-sample test, has better properties. In this case we have $F = 21.13$ and the 5% critical value for the F distribution with 5 and 466 degrees of freedom is 2.23. Therefore we also reject the null using this version of the test.

The main advantage of the White test is that we do not have to decide in advance which of the right-hand side variables is responsible for the heteroscedasticity. In effect auxiliary regressions such as (7.10) should detect heteroscedasticity which is related to any of the original regressors. Examination of the auxiliary regression can also give us useful information on which of the regressors is responsible for any heteroscedasticity which we detect. For example, for equation (7.10), we see that the t-ratios for the estimated coefficients indicates that the employment variables are insignificant while the capital stock variables are highly significant. This indicates that the heteroscedasticity which we detect is due to a relationship between the squared residuals and the capital stock.

7.5 Dealing with heteroscedasticity

We can deal with heteroscedasticity in a number of ways. We have already seen that it does not, in itself, imply that OLS will produce biased coefficient estimates, but that the estimates of the standard errors of the coefficients will typically be biased. Therefore one method of allowing for the effects of heteroscedasticity is to adjust the coefficient standard errors to allow for this. Consider the general model (7.5), it is straightforward to show that $\hat{\beta} - \beta = (X'X)^{-1} X'u$ and therefore

$$
\begin{aligned}
E\left(\hat{\beta} - \beta\right)\left(\hat{\beta} - \beta\right)' &= (X'X)^{-1} X'E(uu')X(X'X)^{-1} \\
&= \sigma_u^2 (X'X)^{-1} X'VX(X'X)^{-1}
\end{aligned}
\tag{7.11}
$$

The problem is that σ_u^2 and V are unknown. However, White (1980) shows that:

$$\sum_{i=1}^{N} \hat{u}_i^2 x_i x_i' \tag{7.12}$$

is a consistent estimator of $\sigma_u^2 X'VX$, where x_i is a $k \times 1$ vector of observations for the right-hand side variables corresponding to observation i. This is the formula used to calculate the White standard errors reported by many regression packages.

As an example, consider estimates of the model (7.8) but with White standard errors replacing the OLS standard errors. This yields the following results:

$$PR_i = -\ 28.64 + 0.004275\ N_i +\ 0.1199\ K_i + \hat{u}_i$$
$$(10.49)\quad (0.00139)\qquad (0.0154)$$

$$R^2 = 0.67 \qquad \hat{\sigma} = 229.7 \qquad F = 493.4 \tag{7.13}$$
$$RSS = 24750928 \qquad\qquad\qquad i = 1,...,472$$

Note that the coefficient estimates and all the statistics other than the standard errors in (7.13) are unchanged relative to (7.8). The White standard errors for both the slope coefficients are higher than the OLS standard errors. This means that confidence intervals based on the White standard errors will be wider and hypothesis test will be less likely to reject any given null hypothesis.

Adjusting the standard errors to allow for the presence of heteroscedasticity means that statistical inference will be more reliable than if we were to rely on the OLS standard errors. However, it does not deal with the problem of the inefficiency of the OLS estimator. One method for dealing with this problem would be to reformulate the model so that heteroscedasticity does not occur. For example, we could express the model in terms of the ratio of profits to capital employed. This makes sense from a statistical point of view since we have already established that there is a relationship between the squared residuals and the capital stock. It also makes sense from an economics point of view since the right hand side variable will become the ratio of profits to capital employed (or the rate of profit) which is a meaningful economic concept. Estimating a regression of this form yields the following results:

$$\left(\frac{PR}{K}\right)_i = \underset{(0.025)}{0.16} + \underset{(0.00039)}{0.0024} \left(\frac{EMP}{K}\right)_i + \hat{u}_i$$

$$R^2 = 0.07 \qquad \hat{\sigma} = 0.49 \qquad F = 36.28 \qquad\qquad (7.14)$$
$$RSS = 112.26 \qquad N = 472$$
$$WHITE = 1.52(0.22)$$

The results of the transformed regression reported in equation (7.14) indicate that transforming the model in this way has effectively eliminated the heteroscedasticity problem. The White test statistic is 1.52 which compares with a 5% critical value for $F_{2,469}$ of 3.015. Therefore, we cannot reject the null hypothesis of no heteroscedasticity at the 5% level. This is confirmed by the p-value for the White test of 0.22 which indicates that we could only reject the null at the 22% level. Although the R^2 for the revised regression is low, it is still the case the slope coefficient is significant as judged by both the t-ratio of $0.0024/0.00039 = 6.2$ and the F statistic of 36.28 which compares with a 5% critical value of 3.9.

7.6 Autoregressive Conditional Heteroscedasticity (ARCH)

The discussion of heteroscedasticity in the previous sections has assumed that the model is estimated using cross-section data. This is because heteroscedasticity is often seen as a purely cross-section problem. However, since the 1980s, there has been a developing literature concerning a type of heteroscedasticity which is relevant for time-series applications – this is the case of Autoregressive Conditional Heteroscedasticity or ARCH. There is a bewildering variety of ARCH models available to researchers and, rather than confuse the reader by trying to provide a comprehensive review, we will concentrate on a particular example which has a wide range of applications. This is the GARCH(1,1) model which is specified below:

$$Y_t = \beta X_t + \varepsilon_t$$
$$\sigma_t^2 = \gamma_1 + \gamma_2 \varepsilon_{t-1}^2 + \gamma_3 \sigma_{t-1}^2 \qquad (7.15)$$

A typical GARCH (Generalised Autoregressive Heteroscedasticity) model consists of two equations: the first is the mean equation which describes the behaviour of the variable Y in terms of a set of conditioning variables X and a random error ε, the second is an equation which describes the *conditional variance* as a function of the squared random error in the previous period and its own lagged value. It is this second equation which we will concentrate on in our discussion.

The key feature of the GARCH model is that the conditional variance is allowed to evolve through time. Thus the assumption of homoscedastic (constant variance) error terms is no longer valid. The conditional variance σ_t^2 in (7.15) depends on the squared lag of the unconditional variance ε_{t-1}^2 and its own lagged value σ_{t-1}^2. Backward substitution in the expression for the conditional variance allows us to write it as:

$$\sigma_t^2 = \frac{\gamma_1}{1-\gamma_3} + \gamma_2 \sum_{i=1}^{\infty} \gamma_3^{i-1} \varepsilon_{t-i}^2 \qquad (7.16)$$

Equation (7.16) shows that the conditional variance can be written as an infinite moving average of past value of the unconditional variance. Note that a necessary, but not sufficient, condition for this sum to converge is $|\gamma_3| < 1$. The fact that this is not sufficient can be seen by examination of the behaviour of the unconditional variance. Note that we can write $\varepsilon_t^2 = v_t + \sigma_t^2$, i.e. the unconditional variance is equal to the conditional variance σ_t^2 plus a residual v_t. Using this expression and substituting into (7.15) we can write the following equation for the unconditional variance:

$$\varepsilon_t^2 = \gamma_1 + (\gamma_2 + \gamma_3)\varepsilon_{t-1}^2 + v_t - \gamma_3 v_{t-1} \qquad (7.17)$$

Equation (7.17) indicates that the unconditional variance follows an ARMA(1,1) process. Moreover, it also demonstrates that, for this process to be stationary, we require $|\gamma_2 + \gamma_3| < 1$.

Example: Consider the following OLS regression in which we have regressed the daily returns[5] from holding Cadbury-Schweppes equity on a constant and the daily returns on the overall market index as measured by the FTSE100.

$$\Delta \ln(CS_t) = 9.78 \times 10^{-5} + 0.58 \; \Delta \ln(FT100_t) + \hat{u}_t$$
$$\quad\quad\quad (4.6 \times 10^{-4}) \quad (0.044) \qquad\qquad (7.18)$$
$$R^2 = 0.12 \qquad \hat{\sigma} = 0.016 \qquad DW = 1.98$$

An ARCH test on the residuals produces the following results:

$$\hat{u}_t^2 = 2.22 \times 10^{-4} + 0.19 \; \hat{u}_{t-1}^2 + \hat{v}_t$$
$$\quad\quad (1.9 \times 10^{-5}) \quad (0.027) \qquad\qquad (7.19)$$
$$TR^2 = 48.32 \qquad F = 50.11$$

Under the null that there is no ARCH effects in the results $TR^2 \sim \chi_1^2$ and since the 5% critical value for the χ_1^2 distribution is 3.84 we reject the null using this test. Similarly, $F \sim F_{1,1300}$ under the null and the 5% critical value for $F_{1,1300}$ is 3.84, meaning that this test also implies rejection of the null. In both cases the test statistic is much larger than the 5% critical value and therefore, it appears that there is strong evidence of ARCH effects in the residuals.

---

[5] The data are daily from 26/10/1995 to 23/10/2000 which gives a total of 1303 observations when weekends and holidays during which no trading takes place are eliminated from the sample.

We can deal with ARCH effects in two ways: we can either adjust the standard errors to allow for their presence or we estimate a model which explicitly allows for ARCH effects. We will consider each method in turn. First, we present a model with 'adjusted' standard errors for the coefficients.

$$\Delta \ln(CS_t) = 9.78 \times 10^{-5} + \underset{(0.055)}{0.58} \ \Delta \ln(FT100_t) + \hat{u}_t$$
$$\underset{(4.25 \times 10^{-4})}{}$$

$$R^2 = 0.12 \qquad \hat{\sigma} = 0.016 \qquad DW = 1.98$$

(7.20)

The results for equation (7.20) are very similar to those shown in equation (7.18). The parameter estimates are identical – the only difference is that the standard errors have been adjusted using the Newey-West procedure. This has increased the standard error for the slope coefficient somewhat which, in turn, means that the confidence interval for the beta parameter will be somewhat wider.

An alternative approach to dealing with ARCH effects in the errors is to estimate a model which explicitly allows for their presence. To do this we will need to assume a specific functional form for the ARCH effects. For example, we could estimate a model of the form (7.15) in which the errors are modelled as a GARCH(1,1) process. The results of doing this are given below in equation

$$\Delta \ln(CS_t) = 3.98 \times 10^{-5} + \underset{(0.035)}{0.62} \ \Delta \ln(FT100_t) + \hat{u}_t$$
$$\underset{(3.86 \times 10^{-4})}{}$$

$$\hat{\sigma}_t^2 = 2.09 \times 10^{-6} + \underset{(0.0065)}{0.04484} \ \hat{u}_{t-1}^2 + \underset{(0.00649)}{0.94906} \ \hat{\sigma}_{t-1}^2$$
$$\underset{(4.52 \times 10^{-7})}{}$$

(7.21)

When we estimate the model with a GARCH error, the parameter estimates for the mean equation do change, though the effects are small. If we examine the variance equation then we see that the sum of the coefficients on the lagged squared residual and the lagged variance term is quite close to one (which would make the equation unstable). However, this is quite a common result in models with GARCH errors.

Exercises for Chapter 7

Exercise 1

An econometrician has estimated the following model which relates inflation to money growth for a sample of 83 economies. The data are average annual values for the period 1980-1993 and are taken from the 1995 *World Development Report*.

```
Ordinary Least Squares Regression Results
Sample period: 1 to 83
Dependent Variable INF
Sample Size 83

Variable            Coefficient         Std Err         T-Ratio

C                     -5.681642        0.704442       -8.065443
MG                     1.046654        0.011553       90.589950

R-squared               0.9902     F-statistic       8206.5392
SEE                     5.657356    RSS            2592.460070
Durbin-Watson           1.7031     LogL           -260.595058
ARCH(1) Test            3.3716     AIC                6.327591
Jarque-Bera            56.2514     SIC                6.385877
```

a) Comment on the regression results and say why the econometrician might argue that the model is both a good statistical fit and consistent with economic theory.

b) The data (which are stored in the workfile INF.TXT) are ordered according to the rate of money growth. Given this you should easily be able to perform the Goldfeld-Quandt test for heteroscedasticity. Construct the test statistic and compare it with an appropriate critical value. What do the results show?

c) Perform the White test for heteroscedasticity. Are the results consistent with the Goldfeld-Quandt test.

d) Set out the implications of your test results for the interpretation of the OLS regression results given above.

Exercise 2

An econometrician has estimated the following market model which relates the daily returns from holding shares in the Tesco company to the daily returns for the overall FTSE 100 index.

```
Ordinary Least Squares Regression Results
Sample period: 2 to 1359
Dependent Variable RET_TESCO
Sample Size 1358
```

Variable	Coefficient	Std Err	T-Ratio
C	0.045903	0.031952	1.436634
RET_MARKET	0.736342	0.032957	22.342221

R-squared	0.2690	F-statistic	499.1748
SEE	1.176692	RSS	1877.524340
Durbin-Watson	2.0885	LogL	-2146.874490
ARCH(1) Test	21.0253	AIC	3.164763
Jarque-Bera	532.8067	SIC	3.172442

a) Comment on the values taken by the slope coefficient and the R^2 for this regression.

b) Is there any evidence for an ARCH process in the residuals? Perform a formal test for the null hypothesis that the residuals do NOT exhibit ARCH.

c) Using the data in the workfile SHARES.IRG, estimate market models for the following companies: AstraZeneca, Lloyds Bank and Vodafone. In each case perform a test for the presence of ARCH in the residuals.

d) What are the implications of your results for the OLS estimates of the market model.

Chapter 8 Stochastic Regressors

8.1: Introduction

Consider the regression model $Y_i = \beta X_i + u_i$. So far we have maintained the assumption that the right-hand side variable X is non-stochastic and therefore that the only source of randomness in this model is the error term u. This is a reasonable assumption in experimental sciences where the X variable consists of an input which is fixed by the person carrying out the experiment. However, it is unrealistic for most economic models in which the X variable is more likely to be a random variable which lies outside the control of the econometrician estimating the equation. The purpose of this chapter is to investigate the implications of working with stochastic regressors and to discuss some methods through which problems associated with this issue can be resolved.

8.2: Implications for Ordinary Least Squares Estimation

Let us consider the OLS estimator derived in an earlier chapter. Using the standard model in mean deviation form $Y_i = \beta X_i + u_i$ we have shown that the OLS estimator of the slope coefficient can be written:

$$\hat{\beta} = \beta + \frac{\sum X_i u_i}{\sum X_i^2} \tag{8.1}$$

To prove unbiasedness, we then applied the expectations operator to (8.1) using two of the standard Gauss-Markov assumptions – that $E(u_i) = 0$ and that X is non-stochastic. The combination of these two assumptions allows us write the expectation of the numerator of the expression on the right-hand side of (8.1) as $\sum E(X_i u_i) = \sum X_i E(u_i) = 0$, thus demonstrating unbiasedness under the Gauss-Markov conditions.

When the X variable is itself stochastic, it is no longer possible to prove unbiasedness in this way. This is because it is not possible to take the X variable outside the expectations operator as in the previous paragraph. Moreover, since in general $E(X_i u_i) \neq E(X_i) E(u_i)$, it is not possible to apply the expectations operator separately to the two stochastic variables in this expression. Consider, for example, the case in which X and u have a joint distribution with a correlation coefficient ρ. In such a case we have $E(X_i u_i) = \rho \sigma_x \sigma_u$ which is clearly non-zero except for the special case $\rho = 0$.

Since it is no longer possible to prove unbiasedness when we relax the fourth Gauss-Markov condition, we instead make use of an alternative concept – that of *consistency*. Consistency is a large sample property and can be thought of as the requirement that the estimator $\hat{\beta}$ should converge towards the true value β as the sample size becomes large. Convergence is defined in terms of the *probability limit* of the estimator. The definition of a probability limit can be stated as follows: $\hat{\beta}$ converges in probability to $\bar{\beta}$ if for any $\varepsilon > 0$ there exists a sample size n which is sufficiently large that the probability that the absolute difference between $\hat{\beta}_n$ and $\bar{\beta}$ exceeds ε is equal to zero. That is, we require:

$$\lim_{n \to \infty} P\left(\left| \hat{\beta}_n - \bar{\beta} \right| > \varepsilon \right) = 0 \tag{8.2}$$

A more concise notation for this is to write $\text{plim} \, \hat{\beta} = \bar{\beta}$ and to note that consistency requires $\text{plim} \, \hat{\beta} = \beta$ where β is the true value of the coefficient.

It is easy to demonstrate that, (1) if an estimator is asymptotically unbiased and (2) if its variance has a limiting value of zero, then the estimator is consistent. Note that these are sufficient but not necessary conditions for consistency. The behaviour of the probability density function for a consistent estimator is illustrated in the Figure 8.1. This shows the PDF for an estimator of a coefficient whose true value is 0.5. Small sample estimates are biased as shown by the peak of their PDF's which lie to the left of the true value. However, as the sample size increases, the peak shifts towards the true value and the variance falls. In the limit, the PDF collapses onto a vertical line passing through the true value of the parameter.

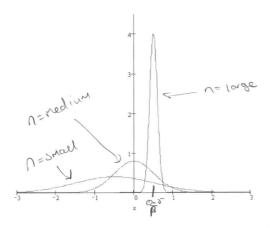

Figure 8.1: Behaviour of the PDF for a consistent estimator

The main advantage of working with probability limits is that they allow a number of mathematical operations which are not possible with the expectations operator. In particular, assuming that a and b are random variables, we have the following:

$$\text{plim}(a \pm b) = \text{plim}(a) + \text{plim}(b)$$
$$\text{plim}(ab) = \text{plim}(a)\text{plim}(b)$$
$$\text{plim}\left(\frac{a}{b}\right) = \frac{\text{plim}(a)}{\text{plim}(b)} \text{ for plim}(b) \neq 0$$
$$\text{plim}(g(a)) = g\,\text{plim}(a)$$

where g is a continuous function which does not involve the sample size n. These properties allow us to demonstrate the consistency of the OLS estimator under a modified set of Gauss-Markov assumptions. In particular, we replace assumption 4 – that the X variable is non-stochastic – with the alternative assumption that it is stochastic but uncorrelated with the random disturbance i.e. $\text{cov}(X,u)=0$. We also need to assume that the sample moments of the joint distribution of X and u converge to their true values i.e.:

$$\text{plim} \frac{\sum X_i u_i}{n} = \text{cov}(X, u) = \sigma_{Xu}$$

$$\text{plim} \frac{\sum X_i^2}{n} = \text{var}(X) = \sigma_X^2$$

Next, consider a transformation of expression (8.1) as shown in equation (8.3):

$$\hat{\beta} = \beta + \frac{(1/n)\sum X_i u_i}{(1/n)\sum X_i^2} \tag{8.3}$$

Applying the standard rules for probability limits yields:

$$\text{plim}\,\hat{\beta} = \beta + \frac{\text{plim}(1/n)\sum X_i u_i}{\text{plim}(1/n)\sum X_i^2} = \beta + \frac{\sigma_{Xu}}{\sigma_X^2} \tag{8.4}$$

and using the modified Gauss-Markov assumption 4 we have $\sigma_{Xu} = 0$, $\sigma_X^2 > 0 \Rightarrow \text{plim}\,\hat{\beta} = \beta$ or that OLS is a consistent estimator. This demonstration generalises easily to the multivariate case.

In the case of stochastic regressors we must rely on large sample properties rather than exact small sample results. However, this creates a problem when it comes to analysing the distribution of estimators since the variance of a consistent estimator goes to zero as the sample size gets large. The usual method for dealing with this problem is to consider the following scaling of the parameter estimator which has a finite positive variance. We have:

$$\sqrt{n}\left(\hat{\beta} - \beta\right) \overset{a}{\sim} N\left(0, \frac{\sigma_u^2}{\sigma_X^2}\right) \tag{8.5}$$

The asymptotic normality of this variable can be demonstrated using the central limit theorem (see the discussion in Greene (1993) for more detail). The property that the variance is non-zero and finite means that this transformation can be used as the basis for a comparison of alternative estimators. However, this is a far as we will take this analysis for the moment.

8.3 The relationship between unbiasedness and consistency

It is tempting the think that, because consistency is a large-sample property, that is a weaker condition that unbiasedness, which holds in small samples. However, this is a mistake. It is possible to demonstrate cases in which an estimator is biased but consistent but it is also possible to demonstrate cases in which an estimator is unbiased but inconsistent.

First consider the case of a biased estimator which is nevertheless consistent. An example here is the following estimator of the slope coefficient from a regression equation:

$$\hat{\beta}_n = \frac{\sum_{i=1}^{n} X_i y_i}{\sum_{i=1}^{n} X_i^2} + \frac{1}{n} \tag{8.6}$$

This is clearly biased since $E\left(\sum_{i=1}^{n} X_i y_i / \sum_{i=1}^{n} X_i^2 + \frac{1}{n}\right) = \beta + \frac{1}{n}$ where c is a non-zero constant. However, we can easily demonstrate that $\text{plim}\,\hat{\beta}_n = \beta$ meaning that the estimator is consistent.

This is illustrated in the Figure 8.2 below in which $Y_i = 0.5X_i + u_i$. From the graphs we see that the estimator has the required properties for consistency in that both the bias and the variance of the estimator go to zero as the sample size gets larger.

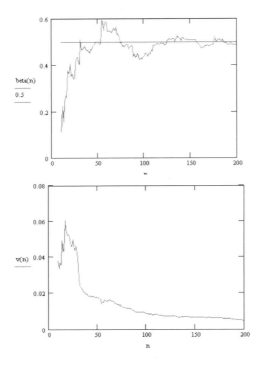

Figure 8.2 Behaviour of parameter estimates and standard deviation for a consistent estimator as the sample size increases

Next consider the OLS estimator of the slope coefficient in the following regression model:

$$Y_t = \beta\left(\frac{1}{t}\right) + u_t$$

The OLS estimator is unbiased by virtue of the fact that $1/t$ is non-stochastic. However, it is inconsistent since $\text{plim}\, 1/T \sum_{t=1}^{T} (1/t)^2 = 0$.

This is illustrated in Figure 8.3. Note that there is no tendency for the estimate of the variance of the coefficient estimate to fall as the sample size gets larger.

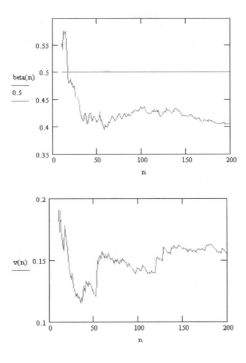

Figure 8.3 Behaviour of parameter estimates and standard deviation for an inconsistent estimator as the sample size increases

This latter case is admittedly very unusual and in most circumstances an unbiased estimator will also be consistent. However, the two concepts are logically separate and, as the examples above show, there is no guarantee that either implies the other.

8.4 Asymptotic Distribution Theory

'Large-sample' or asymptotic results are extremely important in econometrics given the nature of the data which which econometricians are often forced to work. The reason is that the stochastic nature of the regressors precludes the derivation of exact small sample results and we are forced to rely on large sample properties of our estimators. However, the use of large-sample properties creates a number of problems which we discuss below.

One property which we believe estimators should have is that that they should 'converge' on the true value of the parameter of interest as the sample size gets large. Unfortunately, there are several possible definitions of what constitutes such convergence. Three possible definitions are listed below where $\hat{\theta}_n$ is an estimator of an unknown parameter θ based on a sample size n:

$$\lim_{n \to \infty} E\left(\hat{\theta}_n\right) = \theta$$
$$E\left(\sqrt{n}\left(\hat{\theta}_n - \theta\right)\right) = 0 \text{ as } n \to \infty$$
$$\text{plim}\left(\hat{\theta}_n\right) = \theta$$

The first of these simply states that the limit of the expected value of the estimator should equal the true value as the sample size gets large, the second states that the mean of the limiting distribution of $\sqrt{n}\left(\hat{\theta}_n - \theta\right)$ should be zero, while the third states that the probability limit of the estimator should equal the true value. For many 'well-behaved' estimators, all three of these properties will hold. However, it is not difficult to think of examples in which one or more of them can fail. For example, there are cases in which the limit of the expected value simply does not exist. In practice, consistency is often the easiest concept to work with but this does require very strong assumptions.

A second problem which arises when working with asymptotic distributions of estimators is that these are often degenerate. By this we mean that the variance of the estimator goes to zero as the sample size becomes large. Indeed, this is a defining property of a consistent estimator. This creates a problem when it comes to comparing one consistent estimator with another since both have zero variance in large samples. The usual method of dealing with this problem is to work with a transformation of the distribution of the parameter in question which is not degenerate. For example, consider the sample mean as an estimator of the population mean. Assuming a normal distribution, we have $\bar{X}_n \sim N\left(\mu, \sigma_X^2 / n\right)$. This is a degenerate distribution since the variance of the sample mean goes to zero as $n \to \infty$. However, if we consider the transformed variable $\sqrt{n}\left(\bar{X}_n - \mu\right)$, then we can show that $\sqrt{n}\left(\bar{X}_n - \mu\right) \sim N\left(0, \sigma_X^2\right)$ has a non-degenerate distribution. We could therefore base efficiency comparisons of alternative estimators on the distribution of transformations of this kind rather than on the distribution of the estimator itself.

8.5 The Errors in Variables Model

We have now established that correlation between the right-hand side variables of the regression equation and the error term means that ordinary least squares estimates are inconsistent. In this section we consider an important case in which such correlation naturally arises. This is the *Errors in Variables Model* which arises when the right-hand side variables are measured with error.

Consider the following model:

$$Y_i = \beta X_i^* + u_i \tag{8.7}$$

$$X_i^* = X_i + \varepsilon_i \tag{8.8}$$

we assume $\operatorname{cov}\left(X_i^*, u_i\right) = 0$, $\operatorname{cov}\left(u_i, \varepsilon_i\right) = 0$. We would like to be able to estimate (8.7) but we do not observe X^* directly. Instead we observe a proxy variable X which deviates from X^* by measurement error ε. The measurement error is uncorrelated with the error in the regression model and the error in the regression model is uncorrelated with X^*.

What happens if we estimate a regression equation in which the proxy variable is substituted for X^*? This question arises frequently in applied econometrics when economic theory suggests the inclusion of variables for which no data is available and we are forced in such circumstances to rely on proxy variables. Consider the regression equation (8.7), if we substitute for the right-hand side variable using (8.8), then we have the following equation:

$$Y_i = \beta X_i + u_i + \beta \varepsilon_i \qquad (8.9)$$

The error term in (8.9) now comprises the original error term plus an additional component which depends on the measurement error from (8.8). Moreover, we now have a problem since $\text{cov}(X_i, \varepsilon_i) = -\sigma_\varepsilon^2$ since X and ε are correlated. This means that OLS will generate inconsistent estimates.

We can say a bit more about the nature of the inconsistency of the OLS estimates by considering the probability limit of the OLS estimator. Substituting (8.9) into the standard formula for the OLS estimator yields the following expression.

$$\hat{\beta} = \beta + \frac{1/n\sum X_i u_i}{1/n\sum X_i^2} + \beta \frac{1/n\sum X_i \varepsilon_i}{1/n\sum X_i^2} \qquad (8.10)$$

Taking probability limits means that the second term in (8.10) can be discarded since $\text{plim}\frac{1}{n}\sum X_i u_i = 0$ by assumption. However, the third term does not go to zero because of the correlation between X and ε. The probability limit of (8.10) yields the following result:

$$\text{plim}\,\hat{\beta} = \beta\left(1 - \frac{\sigma_\varepsilon^2}{\sigma_X^2}\right) \qquad (8.11)$$

This illustrates several important points. The first is that the OLS estimator will underestimate the true regression parameter when the exogenous variable is measured with error. It also illustrates the point that the size of the inconsistency depends on the size of the variance of the measurement error relative to that of the variance of the explanatory variable X^* (since $\sigma_X^2 = \sigma_{X^*}^2 + \sigma_\varepsilon^2$). Thus, the more 'noise' we introduce into the system in terms of measurement errors, the worse our estimates become. This is an intuitively appealing result and may give us some insights into the circumstances in which the use of proxy variables may be acceptable and those in which they are likely to produce highly misleading results.

Example: The following model was used to generate artificial data sets using a random number generator.

$$X_i^* \sim N(0,1); \quad u_i \sim N(0,1); \quad \varepsilon_i \sim N(0,0.25)$$
$$\text{cov}(X_i^*, u_i) = 0; \text{cov}(u_i, \varepsilon_i) = 0$$
$$X_i^* = X_i + \varepsilon_i$$
$$Y_i = 1.0 + 0.5 X_i^* + u_i$$

1,000 regressions of Y on X were then estimated using the data generated (in each case using a large sample of 1,000 observations). The distribution of the slope coefficient estimates was then examined. The result was an average slope estimate of 0.393. This is extremely close to the theoretically predicted value of the plim of the slope coefficient which can be calculated as $\text{plim}\,\hat{\beta} = \beta(1 - \sigma_\varepsilon^2 / \sigma_X^2) = 0.5(1 - 0.25/(1 + 0.25)) = 0.4$.

8.6 The Instrumental Variables Estimator

We have seen that the OLS estimator is inconsistent when a variable (or variables) on the right-hand side of the equation is correlated with the error term. It therefore becomes important to find alternative estimators with superior properties. One possible alternative estimator is the *Instrumental Variables* (IV) estimator. To construct this estimator we need to find a variable Z which has the properties that it is uncorrelated with the error but *is* correlated with the X variable i.e. $\text{cov}(Z_i, u_i) = 0$ but $\text{cov}(Z_i, X_i) \neq 0$. Now it may not be obvious where such a variable can be found but, if we proceed for the moment on the assumption that we have a suitable Z available, then we can demonstrate the properties of an estimator based around it. The issue of how to find (or construct) such a variable will be considered later.

The estimation problem we have is the standard one of finding an estimator of the unknown slope coefficient of an equation $Y_i = \beta X_i + u_i$. Now an estimator can be constructed using the variable Z which is defined as the *instrument*. The form that the estimator takes can be written:

$$\hat{\beta}_{IV} = \frac{\sum Z_i Y_i}{\sum Z_i X_i} \tag{8.12}$$

Substituting for Y_i and expanding yields:

$$\hat{\beta}_{IV} = \frac{\sum Z_i (\beta X_i + u_i)}{\sum Z_i X_i} = \beta + \frac{1/n \sum Z_i u_i}{1/n \sum Z_i X_i} \tag{8.13}$$

Taking probability limits of the expression for the IV estimator in (8.13) yields $\text{plim} \, \hat{\beta}_{IV} = \beta + \text{cov}(Z_i, u_i) / \text{cov}(Z_i, X_i) = \beta$ since $\text{cov}(Z_i, u_i) = 0$ and $\text{cov}(Z_i, X_i) \neq 0$ by assumption. Therefore, the instrumental variable estimator can be shown to be consistent.

Next consider the variance of the instrumental variable estimator. We have;

$$\left(\hat{\beta}_{IV} - \beta \right)^2 = \left(\frac{\sum Z_i u_i}{\sum Z_i X_i} \right)^2 \tag{8.14}$$

Taking probability limits yields $\text{plim}\left(\hat{\beta}_{IV} - \beta\right)^2 = \sigma_u^2 \sum Z_i^2 / n^2 \rho^2 \sigma_Z^2 \sigma_X^2 = \sigma_u^2 / n\rho^2 \sigma_X^2$ where ρ is the correlation coefficient between X and Z and can be written as $\rho = \text{cov}\left(X_i, Z_i\right) / \sigma_X \sigma_Z$. This shows that , as with OLS estimator, the distribution of the instrumental variable estimator is degenerate since its variance goes to zero as the sample size becomes large. However, multiplication by $\sqrt{n}$ produces a distribution which is not degenerate. In particular, assuming that the errors are normally distributed, means that we can write an asymptotic distribution of the form:

$$\sqrt{n}\left(\hat{\beta}_{IV} - \beta\right) \overset{a}{\sim} N\left(0, \frac{\sigma_u^2}{\rho^2 \sigma_X^2}\right) \tag{8.15}$$

It is clear from (8.15) that the instrumental variable estimator is less efficient that the OLS estimator since the asymptotic variance of $\sqrt{n}\left(\hat{\beta}_{OLS} - \beta\right)$ is σ_u^2 / σ_X^2. The presence of the correlation coefficient in the denominator of the variance term in (8.15) determines the degree of inefficiency. Note that $0 < \rho^2 < 1$ and therefore the variance other IV estimator exceeds that of the OLS estimator. The lower the correlation between x and z (i.e. the closer ρ^2 is to zero) then the less efficient is the IV estimator.

Example: To illustrate the use of the instrumental variable estimator, we repeat the exercise in section 8.5 for the errors in variables model. However, in this case we assume the existence of a variable which has the desired properties for the instrumental variable estimator. (In practice we define a new random variable $Z_i = X_i^* + v_i$ where $v_i \sim N\left(0, 1\right)$). Given the existence of this variable we then estimate 1,000 regressions using the OLS estimator and the IV estimator and compare the distribution of the parameter estimates obtained.

The results of this experiment are shown in Figure 8.6.1 which shows the distributions of the parameter estimates. Once again, the OLS estimator is clearly inconsistent. Even in a large sample of 1,000 observations the average slope coefficient is 0.4004. If we compare this with the distribution of the instrumental variable estimator, then we see that the mean value here is 0.502 which is much closer to the true value of 0.5. However, this reduction in bias comes at a cost. The standard deviation of the OLS estimator is 0.029 which compares with 0.048 for the IV estimator. Thus the mean square error of the OLS estimator is $0.1^2 + 0.029^2 = 0.0108$ whereas that of the IV estimator is $0.048^2 = 0.0023$. Therefore we would still prefer the IV estimator on the mean square error criterion. If correlation between the x and the z variables were lower however, then it is possible that this could be reversed and we might choose the OLS estimator on the MSE criterion, even though it remains inconsistent.

OLS Estimator

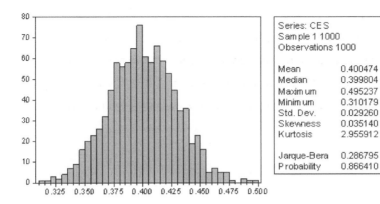

Instrumental Variable Estimator

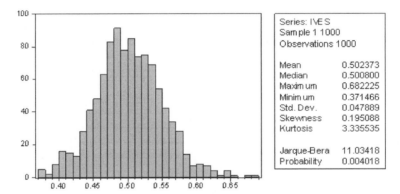

Figure 8.4: Comparison of OLS and Instrumental Variables Estimators in the Errors in Variables Model

8.7 Simultaneous Equations

Another case in which stochastic regressors create problems for estimation is when the equation we estimate comprises one equation drawn from a system of simultaneously determined endogenous variables. To discuss this we will use an artificially generated data set based on a familiar theoretical model. The model we will consider is one consisting of a demand and a supply curve for a commodity. An artificial data set is used to enable a clear exposition of the econometric problems involved. Unfortunately real-world data sets for this problem rapidly become too complicated for a clear presentation of the issues and it is for this reason that we have chosen to use artificially generated data with known properties.

Consider the following model in which q is quantity, p is price, y is variable which affects demand but not supply- for example, income – and w is a variable which affects supply but not demand – for example, the weather. u_1 and u_2 are random errors following unrelated normal distributions.

$$q_t^d = \alpha_1 - \alpha_2 p_t + \alpha_3 y_t + u_{1,t}$$
$$q_t^s = \beta_1 + \beta_2 p_t + \beta_3 w_t + u_{2,t} \qquad (8.16)$$
$$q_t^d = q_t^s$$

For the purposes of this exercise we set $\alpha_1 = 0$, $\alpha_2 = 0.5$, $\alpha_3 = 1$, $\beta_1 = 0$, $\beta_2 = 0.75$ and $\beta_3 = 1$. The variable q and p are endogenous variables (jointly determined within the model) while the variables y and w are exogenous variables (determined outside the model).

Now suppose we wish to estimate the demand curve. The equation $q_t^d = \alpha_1 - \alpha_2 p_t + \alpha_3 y_t + u_{1,t}$ is the structural form of this curve. The structural parameters α_2 and α_3 give the response of demand to price and income. However, if we estimate this equation by OLS then we will obtain biased results. This can be shown by solving the model (8.16) to obtain the reduced form equation for price as shown in equation (8.17)

$$p_t = \frac{\alpha_1 - \beta_1}{\alpha_2 + \beta_2} + \frac{\alpha_2}{\alpha_2 + \beta_2} y_t - \frac{\beta_3}{\alpha_2 + \beta_2} w_t + \frac{u_{1,t} - u_{2,t}}{\alpha_2 + \beta_2} \tag{8.17}$$

It is clear from equation (8.17) that price is a function of the random errors from both the demand and supply curves. Therefore, because $\text{cov}(p_t, u_{t1}) \neq 0$, it follows that the OLS estimator for the structural equation will produce biased estimates of the structural parameters. The following results from our artificially created data set illustrate this point. Note in particular, the estimate of the response of demand to price. The true value of this parameter is -0.5. However, our estimate is only -0.16 and, with a standard error of 0.056, the estimate is more than two standard deviations away from the true value.

```
Ordinary Least Squares Regression Results
Sample period: 1 to 100
Dependent Variable Q
Sample Size 100
```

Variable	Coefficient	Std Err	T-Ratio
C	0.051558	0.085771	0.601108
P	-0.160197	0.056929	-2.813952
Y	0.826905	0.098417	8.402025

R-squared	0.4274	F-statistic	36.2021
SEE	0.847721	RSS	69.707176
Durbin-Watson	1.7922	LogL	-123.850507
ARCH(1) Test	0.6428	AIC	2.537010
Jarque-Bera	1.1216	SIC	2.615165

It is therefore obvious that we will have to make use of some alternative to OLS if we are to obtain consistent estimates of the structural parameters. Note that it is always possible to obtain consistent estimates of the reduced form parameters by OLS. However, these are not the parameters of interest to us. The reduced form parameters are only of interest if they allow us to work backwards to form estimates of the structural parameters.

One possible strategy is to use an instrumental variable estimator. We have already seen that the IV estimator can generate consistent estimates of parameters of interest when we have regressors which are correlated with the error term in our regression equation. As always however, we are faced with the problem of where to find appropriate instruments. We need at least as many instruments as there are right-hand side variables in the equation we wish to estimate. Consider again the model given by (8.16). If we wish to estimate the demand curve then the problem for OLS derives from the correlation of p_t with u_{t1}. What we need is a variable which is uncorrelated with the error in the demand curve but is correlated with the variable for which it is to act as an instrument. In this case an obvious candidate arises in the form of w_t. Because this is an exogenous variable it will be the case that $\text{cov}(w_t, u_{t1}) = 0$. However, changes in w shift the supply curve and therefore affect the price level and therefore $\text{cov}(w_t, p_t) \neq 0$. Let us therefore try using this variable as an instrument for the price level to see if the results improve on those obtained by OLS.

```
Instrumental Variables Regression Results

Sample period: 1 to 100
Dependent Variable Q
Instruments: C Y W
Sample Size: 100
Variable          Coefficient          Std Err          T-Ratio

C                    0.007032          0.113691          0.061851
P                   -0.644567          0.122397         -5.266165
Y                    1.225285          0.152381          8.040899

R-squared         0.8238 E-4          F-statistic          0.0039
SEE                 1.120240          RSS              121.728974
Durbin-Watson       1.5698           LogL            -151.725196
ARCH(1) Test        0.0823           AIC                3.094503
Jarque-Bera         2.0889           SIC                3.172659
```

The IV results reported above show a considerable improvement over the OLS results in terms of the consistency of the estimate of the slope coefficient on price. The point estimate is now considerably closer to the true value of -0.5. However, it should be noted that the standard error of the estimate has increased considerably. This is a general feature of IV estimates in that consistency is always bought at the price of an increase in the variance of the estimate. In other words there is a trade-off between a reduction in bias and an increase in inefficiency when we use an IV estimator for our equation of interest.

The example considered here also illustrates an important point concerning the estimation of structural equations. In order to estimate a structural equation it must be identified. That is, there must be enough information in the model to disentangle the structural parameters from the reduced-form relationships which we actually observe. One way of assessing whether or not this is the case is to check if there are sufficient instruments to use in an IV estimator of the stuctural equation in question. This in turn requires that there should be at least as many exogenous variables present in the model but not included in the equation to be estimated as there are endogenous variables on the right-hand side of the equation. This condition is known as the order condition for identification. It is a sufficient but not necessary condition for identification because there are other possible ways in which the equation might be identified. In practice however, the order condition usually provides a good guide as to whether or not it is even possible to obtain estimates of the parameters of interest.

Note that the example we have given is that of a just identified equation. What this means is that the number of available instruments is exactly equal to the number of exogenous variables on the right-hand side of the equation of interest. If the number of instruments was fewer than the number of endogenous variables then the equation would be under identified and it would not be possible to obtain IV estimates. However, if the number of instruments was greater than the number of endogenous variables then the equation would be over identified. In this case it is possible to obtain IV estimates by using a linear combination of the available instruments. This is often referred to as the two-stage least squares estimator.

Exercises for Chapter 8

Exercise 1

An econometrician has estimated the following equation which relates the growth rate of consumption expenditures to the growth rate of GDP. The data are annual values for the UK economy for the period 1949-2005:

```
Ordinary Least Squares Regression Results
Sample period: 1949 to 2005 (Annual Data)
Dependent Variable DC
Sample Size 57

Variable          Coefficient      Std Err        T-Ratio

C                   0.510273       0.320236       1.593425
DY                  0.847848       0.104289       8.129779

R-squared             0.5458     F-statistic       66.0933
SEE                 1.393300     RSS           106.770715
Durbin-Watson         1.4218     LogL          -98.767020
ARCH(1) Test          0.0561     AIC             3.535684
Jarque-Bera           2.2365     SIC             3.607370
```

a) Explain to your econometrician why the slope coefficient estimate may suffer from the problem of simultaneous equations bias.

b) Using your knowledge of the simple Keynesian income-expenditure model, suggest possible instruments which might be used to construct an instrument variable estimator for the same equation.

Exercise 2

Using the data set NAC.IRG obtain the instrumental variable estimator of the relationship using the change in investment expenditure as an instrument for the change in GDP. What effect does this have on the parameter estimates you obtain?

3. You suggest to the econometrician that there are other possible instruments for GDP growth. In particular, the income-expenditure model assumes that the growth rates of government expenditure and exports are exogenous and are therefore valid instruments. Re-estimate your model using the data in NAC.IRG and using the growth rates of investment, government consumption and exports as instruments in a single regression equation. Does this make a noticeable difference to the regression results?.

Chapter 9: Distributed Lag Models

9.1 Introduction

The statistical theory we have examined so far is appropriate for estimating relationships between variables in equilibrium situations. That is, when the relationship between the variables in the equation is such that there is no tendency for any of the variables concerned to change through time. Unfortunately, this situation is rare when the data we work with consists of time series economic data and we need to develop methods for dealing with what are often called *distributed lag models*. Rather than discussing these in abstract, it is easier to consider a number of examples where such models arise naturally before considering how we go about dealing with them.

First, consider a simple model in which expectations play a role. Suppose we wish to estimate an equation of the form:

$$Y_t = \beta X^e_{t+1} + u_t \qquad (9.1)$$

where the *e* superscript indicates an expectation. Equations like this arise naturally in many areas of economics, particularly in macroeconomics. For example, consumption expenditure is often argued to depend on expectations of income rather than actual income. Another example is the case of price adjustment where the expectations of future inflation enter as one of the determinants of the current rate of inflation in the Phillips curve.

The problem facing the econometrician is that the expectations term in (9.1) is not usually observable directly. Instead we must make use of an auxiliary model for the determination of expectations. One such model is provided by the *adaptive expectations* hypothesis. This states that agents revise their expectations on the basis of past errors made in forecasting the variable in question. We can write down an equation for the determination of expectations as:

$0 < \gamma < 1$

$$X_{t+1}^e - X_t^e = \gamma \left(X_t - X_t^e \right) \text{ or}$$
$$X_{t+1}^e = \gamma X_t + \left(1 - \gamma\right) X_t^e \tag{9.2}$$

The parameter γ determines the speed of adjustment of expectations. A value of γ which is close to zero indicates that expectations take a long time to adjust, while a value of γ which is close to one indicates that expectations adjust rapidly. Using backward substitution we can write the one period ahead expected value of x as a weighted average of past observed values of x. That is:

$$X_{t+1}^e = \gamma \sum_{i=0}^{\infty} \left(1 - \gamma\right)^i X_{t-i} \tag{9.3}$$

Equation (9.3) illustrates why it is important that the expectations adjustment parameter should be less than one. (9.3) is an infinite geometric sum which will only converge if the weights on past values of X decline with time. Now, if we substitute (9.3) into our original equation (9.1) we have an equation in which all the variables are, in principle, observable:

$$Y_t = \beta \gamma \sum_{i=0}^{\infty} \left(1 - \gamma\right)^i X_{t-i} + u_t$$
$$= \beta \gamma X_t + \beta \gamma \sum_{i=1}^{\infty} \left(1 - \gamma\right)^i X_{t-i} + u_t \tag{9.4}$$

We still have a problem in that (9.4) involves an infinite sum of past values of X. Since we only have finite samples available, (9.4) still cannot be estimated directly. However, if we lag (9.4) once and multiply by $\left(1 - \gamma\right)$ then we obtain:

$$(1-\gamma)Y_{t-1} = \sum_{i=1}^{\infty}(1-\gamma)^{i} X_{t-i} + (1-\gamma)u_{t-1} \tag{9.5}$$

substituting (9.5) into (9.4) then yields:

$$Y_t = \beta\gamma X_t + (1-\gamma)Y_{t-1} + u_t - (1-\gamma)u_{t-1} \tag{9.6}$$

The two variables on the right-hand side of (9.6) (X_t and Y_{t-1}) are both observable and therefore (9.6) can, in principle, be estimated. There are some remaining statistical problems to be solved, chief of which is that this transformation has produced a moving average error term. However, it is certainly the case that (9.6) is a lot easier to estimate than either (9.1), which has an unobservable right-hand side variable, or (9.4), which has an infinite number of right-hand side variables. The inclusion of the lagged endogenous variable as a means of obtaining an estimating equation is sometimes referred to as the _Koyck lag_ following its introduction in the work of Koyck in 1954.

The lagged endogenous variable Y_{t-1} is included in equation (9.6) in order to capture a distributed lag effect of the exogenous variable X. In order words, it has been included in order to simplify the equation for the purposes of estimation. However, there are plausible cases in which the inclusion of a lagged endogenous variable arises naturally as part of the derivation of the model. We have already seen an example of this is chapter 6 when we introduced the partial adjustment model. In this chapter we will consider this model in more detail. Let us begin with the assumption that there is an equilibrium relationship between the variables x and y which takes the form:

$$Y_t^* = \beta X_t + u_t \tag{9.7}$$

The variable Y_t^* is the equilibrium or desired value of Y for a given value of X. Let us suppose we are interested in estimating the parameter β which determines the equilibrium response of Y to changes in X. The problem is that equation (9.7) cannot be estimated directly because it contains an unobserved variable Y_t^*.

To enable us to estimate we need to develop a theory of the adjustment process. Now there are many reasons why agents might not immediately adjust the actual value of y to its equilibrium value. In particular, if adjustment is costly (which it almost always will be) then it pays agents to make the adjustment gradually rather than all in one go. As an example, think of the case of a firm adjusting its capital stock in response to an increase in demand for its product. It takes time and resources to install new machinery and it will pay the firm to spread this process out over a period of time rather than attempt to do this immediately. Let us suppose that the agent responds to a gap between the actual and equilibrium values of Y by changing this variable by some fraction of the difference i.e.

$$Y_t - Y_{t-1} = \gamma\left(Y_t^* - Y_{t-1}\right) \tag{9.8}$$

where $0 < \gamma < 1$ measures the fraction of any disequilibrium which is eliminated within one time period. Again, we can think of γ as measuring the speed of adjustment. Values of γ close to zero indicate slow adjustment while values of γ close to 1 indicate fast adjustment. Now if we substitute our equation for the equilibrium value of Y into (9.8) then we obtain:

$$Y_t = \beta\gamma X_t + \left(1 - \gamma\right)Y_{t-1} + u_t \tag{9.9}$$

which only contains observable variables and which can therefore be estimated.

Equations (9.6) and (9.9) are very similar in that both include the current value of x and the lagged value of y on the right-hand side. However, they have been developed from very different theoretical models of the relationship between the two variables X and Y. In the first case the distributed lag relationship arose because y depended on the expectation of x rather than its actual value while in the second case it arose because adjustment of Y towards its equilibrium value was not instantaneous. In principle we might be able to distinguish between the two models by looking at the autocorrelation properties of the residuals – equation (9.6) has a moving average error while equation (9.9) does not. This is not always easy however, particularly in cases where the parameter γ is close to one and therefore the coefficient on the moving average term in (9.6) (i.e. $1-\gamma$) is close to zero. This illustrates an important feature of dynamic economic modelling in that it shows that it is often hard to pin down the exact causes of distributed lag relationships between variables. In real world applications we may observe a distributed lag response but this may be due to a mixture of causes rather than one particular explanation.

Example: The Demand for US Exports

We can illustrate some of the important points in the previous section by the use of an applied example. Suppose we wish to model the demand for US exports. Two plausible explanatory variables are the overall level of trade in the world economy and the real exchange rate for the US relative to other currencies. Therefore we could write an equilibrium relationship of the form:

$$\ln X_t^* = \beta_0 + \beta_1 \ln W_t + \beta_2 \ln E_t + u_t \tag{9.10}$$

where X^* is equilibrium US exports, W is the level of world trade and E is the real effective exchange rate. u is a random error which we assume has the normal classical properties. The equation is written in log-linear terms so that the coefficients can be interpreted as elasticities.

We could estimate (9.10) directly if we assume that the actual level of US exports is always equal to the equilibrium level. However, it is likely that this will produce poor results since this is a highly implausible assumption and, as a result, the estimated equation will suffer from a number of statistical problems, not least of which will be severe serial correlation. This can be seen in Table 9.1 below:

```
Ordinary Least Squares Regression Results
Sample period: 1975.1 to 2008.2 (Quarterly Data)
Dependent Variable LX
Sample Size 134

Variable        Coefficient        Std Err         T-Ratio

C                 -9.062388        0.840733       -10.779158
LW                 1.134321        0.037452        30.287489
LE                 0.208757        0.085625         2.438023

R-squared          0.9532       F-statistic         1334.39
SEE                0.0908
Durbin-Watson      0.5880
ARCH(1) Test      10.7309
Jarque-Bera        2.1212

Autocorrelations

                 AR Coeff         Q-stat      5% crit val

Order 1           0.70256         67.6325          3.841
Order 2           0.78478        152.6612          5.991
Order 3           0.57502        198.6595          7.815
Order 4           0.71839        271.0068          9.488
```

Table 9.1 : OLS estimates of an equilibrium model for US exports

The equation reported in Table 9.1 clearly suffers from serial correlation. This is confirmed by the value of the Durbin-Watson statistic which, at 0.59, is well below the 5% lower bound of 1.63. There is therefore strong evidence of first order serial correlation. This is also confirmed by the Ljung-Box test statistics in the lower part of the table which also indicate the presence of positive serial correlation in the residuals of this model. The implications of this are that, while the coefficient estimates may not be biased, they are certainly inefficient. Moreover, the estimates of the standard errors are most likely biased downwards, meaning that we cannot rely on t-tests for the significance of the individual coefficients or the F-test for their joint significance.

We should also note that the results in Table 9.1 are problematic from the point of view of economic theory as well as their statistical properties. The coefficient for world trade is plausible – it indicates that a 1% rise in world trade is associated with a 1.13% rise in US exports. However, the sign of the coefficient for the real exchange rate runs counter to our expectations. We would expect that an appreciation of the real exchange rate for the dollar should lead to a fall in US exports. Our coefficient estimate is positive indicating that the direction of the effect is counter to the predictions of theory. We should not however, read anything into the apparent significance of this coefficient since this is most likely a product of the underestimation of the standard error due to the presence of serial correlation.

We can attempt to deal with both the economic and statistical problems of our equation by allowing for a distributed lag relationship between the variables. In other words, we acknowledge that the effects on US exports of changes in world trade and the real exchange rate are not instantaneous and we seek to model these explicitly. Let us modify our estimating equation to include the lagged endogenous variable, i.e.

$$\ln X_t = b_0 + b_1 \ln W_t + b_2 \ln E_t + b_3 \ln X_{t-1} + u_t \qquad (9.11)$$

Note that inclusion of the lagged endogenous variable in (9.11) means that the coefficient estimates for world trade and the real exchange rate will no longer provide direct estimates of the equilibrium elasticities. The method for calculating these elasticities will be discussed in the next section of this chapter.

Estimation of equation (9.11) yields the results reported in Table 9.2. These show a noticeable improvement in statistical terms. Note, for example, that the Durbin-Watson statistic has risen from 0.59 for the simple regression to 1.46 in this case. This indicates that extent of the serial correlation has fallen noticeably. This is confirmed by the estimate of the first order autocorrelation coefficient which has fallen from 0.70 to 0.26. Although there is still significant first order autocorrelation, the reduction in the magnitude of the autocorrelation coefficient means that the bias in the standard errors of the coefficients will have been reduced. Moreover, this equation has better properties in terms of economic theory, in that the coefficient on the real exchange rate now has the correct (negative) sign. We will see later that it is possible to improve on this equation further. However, for the moment it does reflect a significant improvement on the simple regression model and emphasises the importance of allowing for a distributed lag relationship between the variables.

```
Ordinary Least Squares Regression Results
Sample period: 1975.2 to 2008.2 (Quarterly Data)
Dependent Variable LX
Sample Size 133

Variable        Coefficient        Std Err         T-Ratio

C                -0.804354        0.256372        -3.137449
LW                0.146736        0.021976         6.677268
LE               -0.038799        0.020021        -1.937932
LAGX              0.861991        0.017511        49.226525

R-squared          0.9976        F-statistic      18195.73
SEE                0.0204
Durbin-Watson      1.4562
ARCH(1) Test       0.0531
Jarque-Bera        8.7943

Autocorrelations

                AR Coeff         Q-stat       5% crit val

Order 1          0.25618         8.9271          3.841
Order 2         -0.03826         9.1277          5.991
Order 3          0.09217        10.3010          7.815
Order 4         -0.15543        13.6636          9.488
```

Table 9.2: Estimates of the Partial Adjustment Model for US Exports

9.2 Assessing the Dynamics

The coefficient estimates in Table 9.2 give us the *impact effects* of changes in the right-hand side variables on US exports. For example the coefficient for LW indicates that a 1% rise in world trade immediately increases US exports by just under 0.15%. Similarly, the coefficient on LE tells us that a 1% appreciation of the real exchange rate immediately reduces US exports by about 0.04%. However, we are often more interested in the long-run or equilibrium effects of changes in the right-hand side variables rather than the impact effects.

An easy way to think about the long-run effects of the exogenous variables is to take equation (9.11) and to solve for the relationships between the variables when they have settled down to an equilibrium. In this case we have:

$$\ln X = b_0 + b_1 \ln W + b_2 \ln E + b_3 \ln X$$
$$= \frac{b_0}{1-b_3} + \frac{b_1}{1-b_3} \ln W + \frac{b_2}{1-b_3} \ln E \tag{9.12}$$

We can therefore solve for the long-run effects by dividing the impact elasticities by a factor equal to one minus the coefficient on the lagged endogenous variable. The impact effect of an increase in world trade can therefore be calculated as:

$$\frac{d \ln X}{d \ln W} = \frac{0.146736}{1-0.861991} = 1.0632 \tag{9.13}$$

Similarly, the long-run elasticity of US exports with respect to the real exchange rate can be estimated as:

$$\frac{d \ln X}{d \ln E} = \frac{-0.038799}{1-0.861991} = -0.2811 \tag{9.14}$$

These long-run elasticities often given enable us to make a better assessment of the economic plausibility of our model. In this case they indicate that the long-run elasticity with respect to world trade is just over 1%, while that for the real exchange rate is about minus 0.3% . Both these numbers are quite plausible from the point of view of economic theory and therefore add to our confidence that this is a reasonable economic model.

The long and the short-run elasticities can be thought of as the end-points of a whole set of dynamic elasticities which determine how the endogenous variable reacts when it is shocked by a change to one of the exogenous variables. The sequence of dynamic multipliers which determine the response to an increase in world trade are illustrated in Figure 9.1. This shows the impact effect as the intercept for $t=0$ with the effects increasing through time and eventually converging on the long-run equilibrium value of 1.0632.

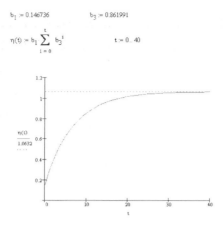

$b_1 := 0.146736$ $b_3 := 0.861991$

$$\eta(t) := b_1 \sum_{i=0}^{t} b_3^i \qquad\qquad t := 0..40$$

Figure 9.1: Dynamic multipliers for an increase in world trade.

One way of assessing the speed of adjustment in dynamic models is to calculate the *half-life* of a shock. This is the length of time it takes for half the adjustment process to be completed. From standard results for geometric progressions we can find the half-life of a shock by finding the value of t such that $b_3^t = 0.5$ or $t = \ln 0.5 - \ln b_3$ which in this case yields $t = 4.667$. Since the data here are quarterly, this indicates that 50% of the adjustment process is completed in just over one year.

9.3 Modelling dynamic relationships

In the example considered in the previous section we showed that the dynamic misspecification identified in a simple regression model could be reduced through the introduction of a lagged endogenous variable into the model. This could be interpreted in economic terms as arising from either the effects of expectations or costs of adjustment. The procedure adopted was therefore to estimate a regression model based on an equilibrium economic model, investigate that model for any evidence of statistical misspecification and then revise the model if necessary. There is an obvious temptation to proceed in this way generally when fitting models to the data but this is a very dangerous strategy for a number of reasons which we now go on to discuss.

The methodology described above is that of *Specific to General* modelling. It is attractive to the economist because it begins with a model which is closely linked to equilibrium economic theory. However, it quickly runs into the problem that almost all such models will be statistically misspecified. This is because economic theory rarely offers a complete description of all the factors which can lead to distributed lag relationships between the variables of the model. Therefore, the specific to general methodology implies that we almost always begin with a misspecified model which creates a number of statistical problems for the investigator. The first problem is that most statistical tests begin with the assumption that we have a well specified model as the basis of our tests. If this is not the case then any tests based on misspecified models are suspect. A second problem is that misspecification of one form can produce multiple types of failure in misspecification tests. For example, a structural break (change in the parameters of model during the sample period) can produce results which appear to show the presence of serial correlation in the model's residuals. Thirdly, there is no unique way of modifying a misspecified model in order to produce a well specified model. Different investigators using the specific to general approach can begin with the same model but end up with very different looking models as they attempt to 'patch up' misspecifications which are detected.

For all the reasons described above, the specific to general methodology is not regarded as good practice among modern econometricians. Instead the *General to Specific* methodology is widely regarded as providing a sounder basis for empirical work. This approach was pioneered by David Hendry in the 1970s and can be summarised as follows:

1. Use economic theory to determine the nature of the equilibrium relationship between a set of variables of interest.

2. Estimate the most general model possible, including many lags of the regression variables so as to maximise the chances of obtaining a statistically well-specified model.

3. Test if it is possible to simplify the model by eliminating irrelevant variables. If the restrictions involved in eliminating variables from the general model are not

rejected, then proceed to the simpler model or *parsimonious specification*, as it is often referred to in this literature.

4. At all stages of the analysis test for evidence of misspecification in the model by examination of the residuals for evidence of serial correlation, heteroscedasticity and other signs that the model does not provide an adequate statistical description of the data.

5. When a parsimonious specification has been identified, test restrictions on the equilibrium relationship between the variables and write the model in a way that can easily be interpreted.

The approach described above sounds simple. However, it still requires judgement and skill on the part of the modeller. What it does do is ensure that the final model will be statistically well specified and this in turn will mean that tests of economic restrictions based on the final model will be more reliable than tests based on misspecified models.

Example: US Export Demand 1976.1 to 2008.2

As an example of the general to specific approach to modelling, we will re-examine our model for US exports. Since our model is estimated using quarterly data we take, as our most general model, an equation which includes the current and four lagged values of the world trade variable and the real exchange rate, as well as four lags of the endogenous variable. When we estimate this general model we obtain the results reported in Table 9.3

```
Ordinary Least Squares Regression Results
Sample period: 1976.1 to 2008.2 (Quarterly Data)
Dependent Variable LX
Sample Size 130
```

Variable	Coefficient	Std Err	T-Ratio
C	-0.505378	0.348252	-1.451184
LW	0.273660	0.058262	4.697088
LAG1W	-0.035315	0.056662	-0.623255
LAG2W	-0.021139	0.054181	-0.390156
LAG3W	-0.028834	0.054971	-0.524529
LAG4W	-0.071893	0.056479	-1.272915
LE	0.146882	0.084385	1.740612
LAG1E	-0.098298	0.107258	-0.916460
LAG2E	-0.069686	0.105435	-0.660937
LAG3E	0.023530	0.106270	0.221420
LAG4E	-0.053352	0.078405	-0.680464
LAG1X	1.051533	0.098425	10.683563
LAG2X	-0.363457	0.133687	-2.718711
LAG3X	0.233897	0.134116	1.743985
LAG4X	-0.037971	0.086186	-0.440575

R-squared	0.9980	F-statistic	4197.12
SEE	0.0191	RSS	0.041846
Durbin-Watson	1.8949		
ARCH(1) Test	0.1726		
Jarque-Bera	6.3615		

Autocorrelations

	AR Coeff	Q-stat	5% crit val
Order 1	0.05159	0.3541	3.841
Order 2	-0.04097	0.5791	5.991
Order 3	0.07760	1.3927	7.815
Order 4	-0.23918	9.1840	9.488

Table 9.3: General dynamic model of US exports

Table 9.3 indicates a model which is reasonably well specified in a statistical sense. The first order serial correlation which was present even in the model with a lagged endogenous variable is no longer evident here. None of the Ljung-Box test statistics are significant at the 5% level (although the test for order 4 comes close). The ARCH test does not indicate any evidence of significant ARCH effects and, while the Jarque-Bera test indicates significant non-normality of the residuals, this can be shown to depend on a few outlying observations.

The problem with the equation reported in Table 9.3 is that it contains too many insignificant variables, i.e. this is not a parsimonious specification. The next stage of the general to specific process is therefore to conduct a specification search in which we eliminate insignificant variables until all variables in the equation are significant at some predetermined level. In doing this it is dangerous to eliminate too many variables at one time because variables which are insignificant in the general model may become significant when other variables are eliminated. It is therefore good practice to eliminate only a few variables at any one time and proceed cautiously until the final specification is obtained. There is no set procedure for the order in which insignificant variables are eliminated but a reasonable rule of thumb is to eliminate the least significant variables first. Gilbert (1986) argues that this is where the judgement and art of econometric model building is introduced. However, significance is not the only criterion, we also need to check if the elimination of variables introduces misspecification problems such as serial correlation.

Following a specification search using the equation in Table 9.3 as a starting point, the final specification for the US export function reported in Table 9.4 was obtained. The stopping criterion for the search was that all variables included should be significant at the 5% level. Note that the lagged world trade and exchange rate variables are not significant at the 5% level. However, they were retained in the final specification because eliminating these variables produced significant serial correlation in the model residuals.

```
Ordinary Least Squares Regression Results
Sample period: 1976.1 to 2008.2 (Quarterly Data)
Dependent Variable LX
Sample Size 130

Variable        Coefficient     Std Err         T-Ratio

C               -0.638760       0.232213        -2.750746
LW               0.165597       0.026207         6.318817
LAG1W           -0.045586       0.031652        -1.440216
LAG2E           -0.033868       0.018460        -1.834646
LAG1X            1.115273       0.085232        13.085106
LAG2X           -0.229673       0.075146        -3.056370

R-squared        0.9979         F-statistic     11654.99
SEE              0.0192         RSS             0.045488
Durbin-Watson    1.9442
ARCH(1) Test     1.1376
Jarque-Bera     11.1745

Autocorrelations

                AR Coeff        Q-stat      5% crit val

Order 1          0.02646        0.0932          3.841
Order 2         -0.12725        2.2641          5.991
Order 3          0.14976        5.2945          7.815
Order 4         -0.16273        8.9008          9.488
```

Table 9.4: US Export Demand – Final Specification

The final specification contains only six estimated coefficients rather than the fifteen in the general model. This is therefore considerably more parsimonious in terms of the variables included. However, the exclusion of nine of the original variables has not reduced the fit of the equation to any noticeable extent. This can be seen by the fact that the R^2 and the standard error of the regression are virtually unchanged. A formal test of all the restrictions involved in moving from the general model to the specific model can be conducted using an F test based on the residual sums of squares of the two equations reported. The test statistic can be calculated as:

$$F = \frac{(0.045488 - 0.041846)}{0.041846} \times \frac{(130 - 15)}{9} = 1.1121$$

The 5% critical value for an F-test with nine and fifteen degrees of freedom is $F_{9,15}^{5\%} = 1.963$. Therefore the restrictions involved in moving from the general to the specific model are not rejected.

General to specific analysis has given us a final equation (Table 9.4) which fits the data well statistically. However, it is less easy to assess whether the equation makes sense from the perspective of economics because of the complex lag structure of the final specification. One solution to this problem is to rewrite the equation in a form in which the parameters can be given a meaningful economic interpretation. A natural format for this is the *error correction model*. This is essentially just a different way of parameterising (or writing) an equation which combines differences and levels of variables so that the investigator can separate out long and short run dynamic effects.

Let us begin by considering the final equation we have estimated. This can be written in the form:

$$\ln X_t = \beta_1 + \beta_2 \ln W_t + \beta_3 \ln W_{t-1} + \beta_4 \ln E_{t-2} + \beta_5 \ln X_{t-1} + \beta_6 \ln X_{t-2} + u_t \qquad (9.15)$$

We can rewrite this equation as:

$$\Delta \ln X_t = \gamma_1 + \gamma_2 \Delta \ln W_t + \gamma_3 \Delta \ln X_{t-1} + \gamma_4 \ln X_{t-1} + \gamma_5 \ln W_{t-1} + \gamma_6 \ln E_{t-2} + u_t \qquad (9.16)$$

Equations (9.15) and (9.16) are formally identical. They are in fact just two different ways of writing the same linear combination of the particular set of variables which are included in the final specification of our model. This can be seen by the fact that there is a unique mapping from the coefficients of (9.15) to (9.16) i.e. $\gamma_1 = \beta_1, \gamma_2 = \beta_2, \gamma_3 = -\beta_6$ $\gamma_4 = \beta_5 + \beta_6 - 1, \gamma_5 = \beta_2 + \beta_3, \gamma_6 = \beta_4$. More importantly, the coefficient of (9.16) have natural economic interpretations. In particular, we can interpret the coefficients on the difference terms as representing short-run dynamics. For example, γ_2 describes the impact effect of an increase in world trade on US exports. The coefficients on the levels terms describe the long-run relationship between the variables. The long-run effect of an increase in world trade is given by the ratio $-\gamma_5 / \gamma_4$. The coefficient on the lagged endogenous variable γ_4 measures the speed of adjustment when the relationship between the variables is different from the equilibrium relationship i.e. it measures the speed with which *errors* (deviations from equilibrium) are *corrected* (by adjustment of the endogenous variable).

At the risk of over emphasising the previous point, it is worth representing our equation in one final way as shown in the figure below:

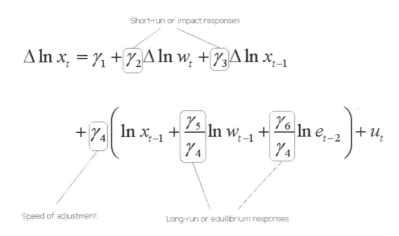

Figure 9.2: Interpretation of the error-correction parameters

Estimates of the final specification of the model in error-correction form are given in Table 9.5. Inspection of this table confirms that this is essentially the same equation as presented in Table 9.4. This can be seen by the fact that the residual sum of squares are identical for the two equations, indicating that these are just two different ways of writing the same linear combination of variables. In fact, many of the equation statistics which are based on the residual sum of squares are identical, including the Durbin-Watson statistic, the standard error of the regression and the Jarque-Bera statistic. However, there are some differences. In particular, the R^2 is much lower for the error-correction representation. This reflects the fact that the reparameterisation of the equation has changed the left-hand side variable from the (log) level of exports to its first difference. Thus the R^2 in Table 9.5 measures the fraction of the variance of the quarter on quarter growth rate of exports which is explained by the model rather than that of the level of exports. This gives a much more realistic guide as to the goodness of fit of the model since it is not artificially increased by the presence of a trend in the series.

```
Ordinary Least Squares Regression Results
Sample period: 1976.1 to 2008.2 (Quarterly Data)
Dependent Variable DX
Sample Size 130

Variable        Coefficient      Std Err        T-Ratio

C                -0.638760       0.232213       -2.750746
DW                0.165597       0.026207        6.318817
DLAGX             0.229673       0.075146        3.056370
LAG1X            -0.114400       0.020334       -5.626021
LAG1W             0.120011       0.023371        5.135023
LAG2E            -0.033868       0.018460       -1.834646

R-squared         0.4656        F-statistic       21.60
SEE               0.0192        RSS            0.045488
Durbin-Watson     1.9442
ARCH(1) Test      1.1376
Jarque-Bera      11.1745

Autocorrelations

                AR Coeff        Q-stat      5% crit val

Order 1          0.02646        11.8944         3.841
Order 2         -0.12725        14.0653         5.991
Order 3          0.14976        17.0957         7.815
Order 4         -0.16273        20.7020         9.488
```

Table 9.5: Estimates of an error-correction model for US exports

If we consider the parameter estimates in Table 9.5, then we see that it provides an economically plausible model of exports. The impact elasticity with respect to world trade is 0.165 which rises to $0.120011 / 0.1144 = 1.049$ in the long-run. The impact elasticity with respect to the real exchange rate is zero because the contemporaneous real exchange rate variable was eliminated during the specification search but there is a long-run effect which is given by $-0.033868 / 0.1144 = -0.296$. The model explains just under half the variation of the quarter on quarter growth rate of exports, which is reasonably impressive when we consider that this is a highly variable series with no trend. Finally, as we have already confirmed for the model in levels, there is no evidence of misspecification other than a significant Jarque-Bera test statistic which indicates some non-normality in the equation residuals.

Exercises for chapter 9

Exercise 1

An econometrician has estimated the following model which relates the demand for airline travel (la) to real personal disposable income (ly) and the relative price of airline travel (lp) for the US economy. The data are annual from 1929 to 2003, the demand for airline travel is defined as revenue passenger miles per head of population and all variables are in natural logarithms.

```
Ordinary Least Squares Regression Results
Sample period: 1929 to 2003 (Annual Data)
Dependent Variable LA
Sample Size 75
```

Variable	Coefficient	Std Err	T-Ratio
C	-24.337050	1.526940	-15.938441
LY	1.750827	0.319720	5.476122
LP	-1.269093	0.546033	-2.324205
R-squared	0.9494	F-statistic	675.7043
SEE	0.546055	RSS	21.468712
Durbin-Watson	0.1013	LogL	-59.511960
ARCH(1) Test	60.0107	AIC	1.666985
Jarque-Bera	54.5418	SIC	1.759685

a) Explain how the slope coefficients for this model can be interpreted as income and price elasticities of demand respectively.

b) Explain why the standard errors of the coefficient estimates are probably too low and suggest an alternative specification which might be less susceptible to this problem.

Exercise 2

Following your advice, the econometrician estimates a partial adjustment model for the demand for air travel. He obtains the following results:

```
Ordinary Least Squares Regression Results
Sample period: 1930 to 2003 (Annual Data)
Dependent Variable LA
Sample Size 74

Variable          Coefficient        Std Err         T-Ratio

C                  -3.303425         0.842850        -3.919350
LY                  0.363260         0.106745         3.403058
LP                  0.262288         0.134519         1.949821
LAGA                0.874940         0.025548        34.246780

R-squared           0.9980        F-statistic      1.1738 E+4
SEE                 0.104433      RSS                0.763449
Durbin-Watson       1.5210        LogL              64.235546
ARCH(1) Test        5.0200        AIC               -1.627987
Jarque-Bera         9.2536        SIC               -1.503443
```

a) Are the coefficient estimates consistent with economic theory?

b) Calculate the long-run income and price elasticities of demand implied by this model.

c) Explain why the use of the Durbin-Watson test for serial correlation is problematic in this case. Using the data in the workfile AIRLINE.TXT, check the Ljung-Box tests for serial correlation and perform the Breusch-Godfrey test. Do these change your conclusions?

Exercise 3

Another econometrician argues that the model should include a time trend to capture the long-term growth of this industry during the estimation period. Re-estimate the partial adjustment model and include a time trend as an additional variable. Does this affect the results noticeably.

Chapter 10: Unit Roots and Cointegration

10.1 Introduction

An understanding of the nature and implications of unit roots is essential for any applied econometrician who works with time series data. However, the topic is rarely considered in introductory statistics modules and, before we can go on to discuss the implications of unit roots, we must therefore define what the term means. We have already seen that time series models can be written down using the lag operator. For example. If we have:

$$X_t = \gamma_1 X_{t-1} + \gamma_2 X_{t-2} + u_t \qquad (10.1)$$

where X is the variable of interest and u is a random variable or 'shock' to X which is assumed to have the standard classical properties for an error i.e. it is assumed to have zero mean, constant variance and to be independent of its own past values. (10.1) can be written as:

$$X_t \left(1 - \gamma_1 L - \gamma_2 L^2\right) = u_t \qquad (10.2)$$

where L is an operator which has the effect of lagging the x variable one time period. Therefore $LX_t = X_{t-1}$ and $L^2 X_t = X_{t-2}$. One of the advantages of writing a model in this form is that we can manipulate the lag operator exactly as we would any variable in an equation. For example, the *lag polynomial* in equation (10.2) is quadratic in L and we can therefore solve it in exactly the same way as we would any quadratic equation to obtain the following:

$$\left(1 - \gamma_1 L - \gamma_2 L^2\right) = \left(1 - \beta_1 L\right)\left(1 - \beta_2 L\right) \qquad (10.3)$$

The values of β_1 and β_2 obtained are referred to as the *roots* of the lag polynomial. These roots may be either real or a pair of complex conjugates. If the roots are real and if either is equal to one then the series x is said to contain a unit root. In the event that both roots are real and equal to one then the series is said to contain a double unit root. If the roots are complex then the series can still be said to contain a unit root if the real part of the complex conjugate is equal to one.

The presence of a unit root in a time series has important implications for statistical analysis. To illustrate this, let us consider the simpler example of a first-order autoregressive process:

$$X_t = \beta X_{t-1} + u_t \qquad (10.4)$$

By a process of backward substitution this can be written as:

$$X_t = \sum_{i=0}^{\infty} \beta^i u_{t-i} \qquad (10.5)$$

This illustrates a very important result in time series analysis which is that any finite autoregressive process can be written as a infinite moving average of past errors. Now, if the coefficient β is less than one in absolute value, the weights on past errors will decline the further in the past is the error. This is because $\beta^i \to 0$ as $i \to \infty$. However, if the coefficient $\beta = 1$, then the weights do not decline. This means that the influence of a random shock to the process continues to have just as much influence on its current value no matter how long ago the shock occurred.

Classical statistical theory requires that the random variables we analyse be *stationary*. The definition of stationarity is that the moments of the distribution of the random variable, such as its mean and variance, should be finite and constant. Now consider the mean and the variance of the random variable X. From (10.5) we have that:

$$\mu_x = \sum_{i=0}^{\infty} \beta^i E\left(u_{t-i}\right) = 0 \qquad (10.6)$$

since $E\left(u_{t-i}\right) = 0$ for all values of i. Note that this holds whatever the value of β. The problem for a unit root process arises with the variance rather than the mean of the series. We have:

$$\sigma_x^2 = \sum_{i=0}^{\infty} \beta^2 E\left(u_{t-i}^2\right) \qquad (10.7)$$

(we can ignore cross-product terms of the form $u_{t-i}u_{t-j}$; $i \neq j$ because of the assumption that the shocks are not serially correlated). Now if $|\beta| < 1$, that is if the series does *not* contain a unit root, then we can easily see that the infinite sum in (10.7) converges to a finite limit. In fact we have $\sigma_X^2 = \sigma_u^2 / \left(1 - \beta^2\right)$ since $E\left(u_{t-i}^2\right) = \sigma_u^2$ because of the assumption of constant variance of the shocks. However, if the series *does* contain a unit root, i.e. $\beta = 1$, then we have a problem in that the infinite sum in (10.7) does not converge and therefore the variance of x is not defined. It follows that the variable x is not stationary and therefore that the standard results of classical statistical theory do not apply.

It is hard to overstate the implications of non-stationarity for statistical analysis. All the standard testing procedures we are used to applying depend on distributions which assume that the random variables being considered are stationary. Once we remove this assumption, none of the standard distributions apply and we are unable to calculate hypothesis tests, confidence intervals or any of the usual statistical procedures on which we rely. It therefore becomes extremely important to identify when unit roots are present and also to develop a strategy for dealing with unit roots when we detect them.

Before we discuss how to test for the presence of a unit root in a given series, we first need to draw attention to a special case which is extremely important for the analysis of economic time series. This is the case of a series which grows through time. Many economic time series exhibit trend growth. This, in itself, means that they cannot be stationary in the conventional sense because their mean or expected value will increase through time. In a trivial sense this means that such series contain a unit root. However, it is possible that this can be dealt with in a very simple way. For example consider a variable X which is determined by the following process:

$$X_t = \alpha + \beta t + u_t \tag{10.8}$$

This is non-stationary since $\mu_X(t) = E(X_t) = \alpha + \beta t$. However, the mean of X is a deterministic function of time and, if we allow for this appropriately, then in all other respects x behaves like a stationary variable. For example, if we consider the transformed variable $Z_t = X_t - \alpha - \beta t$, then z behaves as a stationary variable with zero mean and constant variance ($= \sigma_u^2$). A variable like (10.8) is said to follow a *deterministic trend process*.

The problem is that (10.8) is not necessarily the appropriate model for all series which grow through time. An alternative might be to consider a model like that defined in equation (10.9)

$$X_t = \beta + X_{t-1} + u_t \tag{10.9}$$

This is the case of a *random walk with drift*, the drift being provided by the constant term β which means that the expected value of x will increase by this amount with every time period. In some ways (10.9) behaves rather like (10.8) in that the expected value of x will increase by a factor β with every time period. Thus in both cases the series x will have trend component. In fact (10.9) is often described as a *stochastic trend process*. However, (10.9) behaves very differently when we come to consider the variance of series around the trend.

To see the difference between deterministic and stochastic trend processes, we will consider the mean and the variance of a forecast k periods into the future. For the deterministic trend process we have $E(X_{t+k}) = \alpha + \beta(t+k)$ or alternatively $E(X_{t+k} - X_t) = \beta \times k$ (assuming that u_t is not observed at the time the forecast is made). Similarly for the stochastic trend process we also have $E(X_{t+k} - X_t) = \beta k$ meaning that the central forecast is identical. However, the forecast variances for the two cases are very different. For the trend stationary process we have $E(X_{t+k} - E(X_{t+k}))^2 = \sigma_u^2$, that is the forecast variance is equal to the variance of the error term in (10.8). This is because built into the trend stationary process is the assumption that the variable X will always return to a predetermined path given by the deterministic part of (10.8). In contrast, the forecast variance for the stochastic trend process is given by $E(X_{t+k} - E(X_{t+k}))^2 = k\sigma_u^2$. Here the forecast variance increases in proportion to the length of time into the future we wish to forecast. This difference means that there is an important difference between the two processes when we interpret forecasts and therefore it is important to be able to distinguish empirically between them.

10.2 Detection of unit roots

We now turn to the issue of testing for the presence of a unit root in a given time series. In principle we could test for the presence of a unit root by estimating a regression equation of the form:

$$X_t = \beta_1 + \beta_2 X_{t-1} + u_t \qquad (10.10)$$

and testing the null hypothesis $H_0 : \beta_2 = 1$ against the one sided alternative that $H_1 : \beta_2 < 1$. However, it easier to reformulate equation (10.10) to:

$$\Delta X_t = \gamma_1 + \gamma_2 X_{t-1} + u_t \qquad (10.11)$$

$\sigma_u^2 / (1 - \beta^2)$ where $\gamma_1 = \beta_1$ and $\gamma_2 = \beta_2 - 1$ so that we can test the null hypothesis that $H_0 : \gamma_2 = 0$ against $H_1 : \gamma_2 < 0$. A natural test statistic here is the t-ratio for the coefficient on x_{t-1} i.e. $\tau = \hat{\gamma}_2 / SE(\hat{\gamma}_2)$ but we immediately run into a problem in that, under the null hypothesis, the series in question is not stationary. This means that the standard distributional results of classical statistical theory do not apply and we cannot therefore use the standard t-tables as a basis for judging whether τ is statistically different from zero. In fact, it has proved impossible to derive a theoretical distribution for this test statistic and we must instead use critical values for this test which are determined by Monte Carlo methods. The first such critical values were derived by Dickey and Fuller (1979). However, the most reliable critical values are those provided by MacKinnon (1991). These are presented in the form of *response surfaces* or functions of the same size. For equation (10.11) the 5% critical values can be derived from the following function:

$$C(T) = -2.8621 - \frac{2.738}{T} - \frac{8.36}{T^2} \tag{10.12}$$

where T is the sample size. For example, for a sample size of 50, the 5% critical value is -2.92. This is considerably larger (in absolute terms) than the 5% critical value for a t-test which would be about -1.64 for a one sided test. MacKinnon's response surfaces allow the calculation of critical values for a range of specifications and size of the test as well as allowing for variation of the sample size.

If there is a trend in the series then we need to allow for this in the specification of the equation we use to test for the presence of a unit root. To do this we estimate an equation of the form:

$$\Delta X_t = \gamma_1 + \gamma_2 X_{t-1} + \gamma_3 t + u_t \tag{10.13}$$

The test statistic is still the t-ratio $\hat{\gamma}_2 / SE(\hat{\gamma}_2)$ but again this will not follow a standard t-distribution. MacKinnon again provides response surfaces for the critical values which in this case take the form:

$$C(T) = -3.4126 - \frac{4.039}{T} - \frac{17.83}{T^2} \qquad (10.14)$$

The 5% critical value for a sample size of 50 in this case is therefore -3.50.

Another complication which arises when testing for unit roots is the presence of serial correlation in the testing equation. Equations (10.10) and (10.13) are appropriate if the series X follows a first order process. However, if X follows a higher order autoregressive process then it becomes necessary to augment the equation with lags of the difference of X in order to avoid serial correlation in the residuals of the testing equation producing a bias in the test statistic. This means that in most practical applications we make use of the *Augmented Dickey Fuller test equation* which takes the form:

$$\Delta X = \gamma_1 + \gamma_2 X_{t-1} + \gamma_3 t + \sum_{i=1}^{p} \gamma_{3+i} \Delta X_{t-i} + u_t \qquad (10.15)$$

Equation (10.15) is the most general form of the equation which includes a constant and a time trend as well as the lag of x and the lagged differences of X The lag length p is chosen to be sufficiently long so as to eliminate any serial correlation in the estimating equation. In practice p is often chosen by reference to one of the measures of goodness of fit such as the Schwartz Information Criterion.

Example: Suppose we wish to test if real GDP for the UK contains a unit root. The first stage of the process is to examine the series to see if it contains a trend. This will determine which Dickey-Fuller test we use. A graph of the series indicates that a trend is present (see Figure 10.1) and therefore the most sensible strategy is to use a test equation which includes a time trend as the basis of our test. It would not make sense in this case to estimate a test equation which did not include a time trend since this would have no way of capturing the fact that, over time, GDP generally increases.

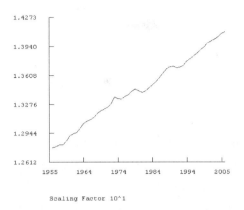

Scaling Factor 10^1

Figure 10.1: UK Real GDP 1955 to 2005

The null hypothesis here is that the series is NOT stationary i.e. $\gamma_2 = 0$. Therefore a rejection of the null means that a unit root is not present in the data or that real GDP is stationary around a linear trend. The test is based on the estimated equation given in Table 10.1. One lagged difference term is included since this can be shown to minimise the Schwartz criterion.

```
Ordinary Least Squares Regression Results
Sample period: 1955 to 2005 (Annual Data)
Dependent Variable DY
Sample Size 51

Variable        Coefficient      Std Err       T-Ratio

C                 2.827257      0.938813      3.011524
TREND             0.005262      0.001766      2.980420
LAGY             -0.223875      0.074788     -2.993468
D1Y               0.405576      0.131677      3.080082

R-squared         0.2363      F-statistic         4.85
SEE               0.0162      RSS             0.012361
Durbin-Watson     1.7914      LogL          139.923270
ARCH(1) Test      4.3565      AIC            -5.330324
Jarque-Bera       3.5008      SIC            -5.178809
```

Table 10.1 Test Equation for Unit Root in Real GDP

The test statistic here is the 't-ratio' for lagged real GDP which takes the value -2.99. This needs to be compared with the 5% critical value determined by the MacKinnon response surface which can be calculated as -3.498. Therefore, in this case, we cannot reject the null hypothesis at the 5% level and we conclude that a unit root is present in real GDP.

It is interesting to note that it would have been very difficult to assess if there was a unit root in the series simply by examining a graph of the series. Examination of the graph of the series in Figure 10.1 indicates that a trend is present but it is extremely difficult to assess whether this is because of the presence of a deterministic or a stochastic trend. The result here is also consistent with a number of other studies which have found evidence of unit roots in the main national accounts aggregates. An important early contribution to this literature is the paper by Nelson and Plosser (1992) which has been followed by many other papers reporting similar findings.

For a second example, we will consider a case in which a trend is not present in the data. The series we will consider is 'Stockbuilding' or inventory accumulation for the UK economy over the period 1955 to 2005. The graph of the series shown in Figure 10.2

confirms that this series does not exhibit an obvious trend. However, it is still possible that this series might contain a unit root if it follows a random walk process without a drift term.

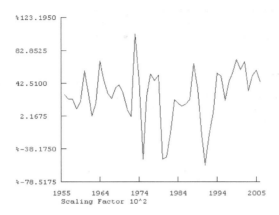

Figure 10.2 Stockbuilding £m 2005 prices

In this case the natural test equation to estimate includes a constant but no time trend. The inclusion of a time trend is not necessary to capture trend growth in the series and would reduce the power of the test by increasing the critical value and making it harder to reject the null hypothesis even when the null is false. The equation used to construct the test therefore takes the form:

```
Ordinary Least Squares Regression Results
Sample period: 1955 to 2005 (Annual Data)
Dependent Variable DSB
Sample Size 51

Variable        Coefficient        Std Err         T-Ratio

C               1343.691999        450.838131       2.980431
LSB               -0.787705          0.149836       -5.257114
D1SB               0.319691          0.137603        2.323279

R-squared          0.3694        F-statistic        14.06
SEE             2718.1233        RSS            3.536 E09
Durbin-Watson      1.8996        LogL          -474.112482
ARCH(1) Test       0.0461        AIC             18.710293
Jarque-Bera        3.9376        SIC             18.823930
```

Table 10.2: Test equation for unit root in stockbuilding

In this case the test statistic is -5.26 which compares with a critical value of   -2.92 taken from the MacKinnon response surfaces. Therefore we reject the null hypothesis in favour of the alternative that the series is stationary.

10.3 Unit Roots and Spurious Regressions

We have seen that one of the implications of time series that contain a unit root is that we can no longer rely on the distribution theory of classical statistics. This is a particular problem when we wish to look at the relationship between different variables which contain unit roots and has given rise to the problem labelled *spurious regression*. A spurious regression is one which appears to show a significant relationship between two or more variables but in which this appearance is not genuine. Spurious regressions can arise when the variables in the regression equation contain unit roots but it is also important to realise that this is not the only possible cause of the problem.

The potential for random walk series to lead to spurious regression problems was first argued in a paper in the Journal of Econometrics by Granger and Newbold (1974). This is a vitally important paper in the history of applied econometrics in that it changed the direction of econometric practice. Although this paper predates the unit root and cointegration literatures it can be argued that it set out the issues and questions which subsequently led to the development of these literatures.

One of the interesting features of the Granger and Newbold paper is that it marks an early example of the use of Monte Carlo analysis to both demonstrate and develop a theoretical point. Although the main argument concerning spurious regressions is developed theoretically, it is possible to argue that the paper might not have had the same impact if the authors had not presented simulation results which dramatically illustrated their point. Monte Carlo analysis involves the use of simulated regression results on data which is generated artificially using a random number generator. It provides a valuable element in the modern econometrician's toolkit in that it allows the investigation of the distribution of test results in cases when theoretical results are too difficult, or even impossible, to obtain. The spurious regression result provides an excellent example to illustrate this method.

Granger and Newbold's Monte Carlo analysis begins with the generation of artificial random walk time series of the form:

$$
\begin{aligned}
Y_t &= Y_{t-1} + \varepsilon_{t1} \\
X_t &= X_{t-1} + \varepsilon_{t2}
\end{aligned}
\tag{10.16}
$$

where ε_1 and ε_2 are independent $N(0,1)$ variables. They estimate a regression equation of the form:

$$
Y_t = \alpha + \beta X_t + u_t
\tag{10.17}
$$

and assess if the t-ratio $\hat{\beta} / SE(\hat{\beta})$ is greater than the 5% critical value. This process is repeated a large number of times using different drawings of the random variables ε_1 and ε_2.

In the following table, the Granger-Newbold exercise has been replicated using an EViews programme and the EViews random number generator. Table 10.1 confirms that the Granger and Newbold results, even though the number of simulations has been increased from 100 in their study to 1,000 in this case. The percentage of rejections is somewhat lower than they find (66.8 rather than 76) but the average Durbin-Watson statistic and adjusted R^2 statistics are remarkably close to their values of 0.32 and 0.26 respectively.

	% H_0 rejections	Average DW Statistic	Average $\bar{R}^2$
Granger and Newbold results (100 replications)	76	0.32	0.26
Replication of Granger-Newbold results (1,000 replications)	66.8	0.34	0.22
Series generated as random walk with drift $y_t = 0.5 + y_{t-1} + \varepsilon_{t1}$ $x_t = 0.5 + x_{t-1} + \varepsilon_{t2}$	99.6	0.36	0.84
Series generated as random walk with drift plus trend in regression equation $y_t = \beta_1 + \beta_2 x_t + \beta_3 t + u_t$	50.9	0.50	0.93
Series generated as random walk with drift plus regression equation estimated in difference form	5.0	1.99	-0.0016

Table 10.3 Monte Carlo Simulations of Random Walk Regressions

Table 10..3 also presents a number of further Monte Carlo simulation which are designed to illustrate some additional points. First, in row 3 of the table, the processes generating the values for Y and X have been changed to random walks with drift rather than simple random walks. This is arguably more consistent with real world economic data where the random walk with drift is often a very good first approximation to the behaviour of economic time series. The effect of this is to make the spurious regression problem significantly worse. The percentage of rejections of $H_0 : \beta = 0$ rises to 99.6% and, although there is little effect on the average Durbin-Watson statistic, the average $\bar{R}^2$ has risen to 0.84. In the next row, we experiment by adding a deterministic trend to the regression equation to see if this reduces the proportion of spurious regressions. Although there is some reduction if the percentage of rejections of $H_0 : \beta = 0$ to 50.9% this is still well above the correct level of 5% for the significance level chosen. In the final row, we experiment by changing the regression equation to one in differences rather than levels. This does bring the percentage of false rejections down to the correct level and also produces an average Durbin-Watson statistic which is consistent with regression residuals which are not serially correlated as well as an average value of $\bar{R}^2$ which is close to zero.

10.4 Cointegration

The potential for unit roots in variables to create spurious regressions is an uncomfortable problem for econometricians. We could simply take first differences of the data before estimation but this ignores the possibility that there might be genuine relationships between the levels of the series in question. For example, we might find that there is a long-run equilibrium relationship between two variables such as the level of consumption expenditure and income. If the ratio of consumption to income rose above its equilibrium value then it would tend to fall back towards this value over time. Differencing the data prior to estimation means that equilibrium relationships such as this would never be detected. Moreover, long-term equilibrium relationships of this kind would add important information to economic models which would improve both their simulation properties and forecasting ability

If we are to detect equilibrium relationships between the levels of variables then we need to introduce the idea of *cointegration*. We can define an integrated variable as one which needs to be differenced in order to make it stationary. The *order of integration* is the number of times differencing must be performed in order to make this so. Thus, for example, a series which is integrated of order one (written $I(1)$), contains a single unit root and must be differenced to produce a stationary ($I(0)$), series. Many economic time series can be shown to be $I(1)$ and occasionally we find series which are $I(2)$ and which must therefore be differenced twice to produce a stationary series. However, it is very rare to find series which have a higher order of integration than two with the kinds of data we deal with as econometricians.

Now, let us assume that we have two series X and Y which are individually $I(1)$, that is each series contains a single unit root. A linear combination of these two series can be written:

$$Z_t = \alpha_1 Y_t + \alpha_2 X_t \qquad (10.18)$$

In most cases we would expect that a linear combination of two $I(1)$ series would itself be $I(1)$. However, in certain special cases it is possible that combining two such series may produce an $I(0)$ or stationary series. If this is the case then we say that there exists a *cointegrating relationship* between the series. This means that, even though each individual series must be differenced to render it stationary, we can form a linear combination of the series which is already stationary.

It is important to note that a cointegrating relationship will not necessarily exist between any two non-stationary variables. Indeed, this will tend to be the exception rather than the rule. However, in cases where such a relationship does exist, it is potentially very useful for the econometrician modelling the relationship between the series. What it means is that we can write down (and hopefully estimate) a meaningful relationship between the levels of series which individually contain unit roots. That is, the relationship in levels between two such series will reflect a genuine economic relationship rather than a spurious regression. In addition, linear regression is likely to provide a good way of estimating the weights in such a relationship. This is because the least squares estimator minimises the residual sum of squares and the residual sum of squares for a linear combination of variables which is stationary will always tend to be lower than a combination which is non-stationary.

Let us consider, as an example, the equation we estimated for US export demand in chapter 9. When we regress exports on world trade and the real exchange rate, then the residuals define a linear combination of the variables as given in equation (10.19)

$$\hat{u}_t = lx + 9.062388 - 1.13432\ lw - 0.208756\ le \qquad (10.19)$$

Note that we have not bothered to reproduce regression statistics such as the standard errors of the coefficients or the t-ratios because we know that these are biased. All we are interested in here are the values of the regression coefficients which define the (possible) equilibrium relationship between the variables or, as it is often referred to, the *cointegrating vector*. Note also that the coefficient for *lx* has been fixed at one rather than estimated. This does not affect the properties of the cointegrating vector since we could multiply every variable which appears in (10.19) by an arbitrary non-zero constant without changing its properties. The only effect this would have would be to rescale the data.

Is (10.19) a cointegrating relationship? To answer this we must assess if this linear combination is stationary. A useful first step is often to graph the series to identify any possible trends. In this case a plot of the residuals produces the results shown in Figure 10.3. This shows no obvious trend in the series. However, a definitive decision on whether this series is stationary must be deferred until we have developed a formal testing procedure.

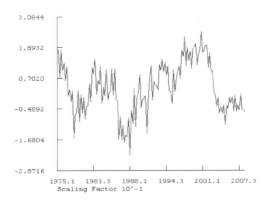

Figure 10.3: Residuals from the US export demand function

10.5 Testing for Cointegration

Many different tests for cointegration have been suggested to the extent that a complete book would be needed to treat all of them thoroughly. Rather than even try to give a complete treatment, we will consider the three testing procedures which are most widely used in the applied econometrics literature. These are the firstly - the Engle-Granger two-step procedure, secondly - tests based on error-correction equations and finally, the Johansen procedure.

10.5.1 The Engle-Granger Two-Step Procedure

The Engle-Granger procedure is both simple and intuitively appealing. If we wish to test for a cointegrating relationship between a set of variables then we first calculate a simple OLS regression. We then perform a unit root test on the residuals from this regression. The null here is that the residuals are NOT stationary and therefore we would only conclude that there exists a cointegrating relationship if we reject the null in the second stage regression. Testing for a unit root in the residuals from an OLS regression is complicated by the fact that the critical values are not the same as we would apply for a standard unit root test. However, MacKinnon (1991) provides response surfaces which allow us to calculate appropriate critical values easily and so this is a relatively easy problem to solve.

Using the residuals for our US export demand equation (10.19) we obtain the second stage regression shown in Table 10.4 The test statistic is the τ statistic, or the 't-ratio' for the lagged residual, but once again this does not follow a standard t-distribution. A value of -2.24 would lead us to reject the null using the 5% t-distribution critical values. However, the MacKinnon 5% critical value for this case is -3.81 which indicates that we are quite some way from rejecting the null in this case. As things stand therefore, we cannot state with any conviction that there is a cointegrating relationship between these variables.

```
Ordinary Least Squares Regression Results
Sample period: 1976.1 to 2008.2 (Quarterly Data)
Dependent Variable DRES
Sample Size 130

Variable          Coefficient        Std Err        T-Ratio

C                  -0.002322        0.004520       -0.513883
LAGRES             -0.122349        0.054591       -2.241173
D1RES              -0.576485        0.071825       -8.026169

R-squared             0.4307     F-statistic       48.0526
SEE                0.051521     RSS              0.337117
Durbin-Watson        1.7848     LogL          202.603790
ARCH(1) Test         0.2124     AIC             -3.070827
Jarque-Bera          0.1888     SIC             -3.004653
```

Table 10.4: Test for a cointegrating relationship for US exports

Although the Engle-Granger test has considerable appeal because of its simplicity, it does suffer from a number of problems. In particular, it can be shown that this test is likely to have *low power*. That is, the probability of a Type II error is large in that it will be hard to reject the null hypothesis even when the null hypothesis is false. Therefore other tests for cointegration have been developed which we now go on to discuss.

10.5.2 Tests based on Error-Correction Equations

In chapter 9 we showed how an error correction equation could be estimated for US exports which combined both short-run adjustment and a long-run relationship between the variables. The long-run relationship which is implicit in an error-correction model can be thought of an estimate of the cointegrating relationship between the variables. Moreover, because the error-correction model captures the short-run dynamic relationship between the variables, it will provide more efficient estimates of the cointegrating parameters and therefore will act as the basis for a more powerful test for the existence of a cointegrating relationship.

To consider how we might use the this approach as the basis for a test for cointegration, we first consider a generic error-correction model of the form:

$$\Delta Y_t = \gamma_1 + \gamma_2 \Delta X_t + \gamma_3 \left(Y_{t-1} - \beta X_{t-1} \right) + u_t \tag{10.20}$$

This equation contains only two variables and has very simple dynamics. However, it can easily be extended to more general cases. The cointegrating parameter here is β and the 'speed of adjustment' coefficient is γ_3. If we estimate this equation by OLS then the equation we estimate would take the form:

$$\Delta Y_t = b_1 + b_2 \Delta X_t + b_3 Y_{t-1} + b_4 X_{t-1} + u_t \tag{10.21}$$

and we would calculate an estimate of β as $-\hat{b}_4 / \hat{b}_3$. Note that the estimated coefficient $\hat{b}_3$ still gives us a direct estimate of the speed of adjustment.

Now there are two ways in which we could an estimated equation of the form (10.21) to construct a test for cointegration. The first is to base the test around the speed of adjustment coefficient. If the series are not cointegrated then there should be no tendency for any return to an equilibrium relationship in levels and therefore γ_3 should be zero. We could therefore base our test on the null hypothesis $H_0 : b_3 = 0$ against the alternative that $H_1 : b_3 < 0$. Critical values for a test of this form have been calculated by Ericsson and MacKinnon (1992). Another test might be based on the *joint* significance of the levels terms Y_{t-1} and X_{t-1} in equation (10.21) since, if the variables are not cointegrated levels terms should be irrelevant in explaining the first difference of the series y. This test was first put forward by Pesaran, Shin and Smith (2001) and response surfaces for the critical values have been calculated by Turner (2006).

To apply these tests to our example for US exports, we first estimate the error-correction equation. This takes the form:

$$\Delta lx_t = -\ \underset{(0.2322)}{0.6388} + \underset{(0.0262)}{0.1656}\ \Delta lw_t + \underset{(0.0751)}{0.2297}\ \Delta lx_{t-1}$$
$$-\ \underset{(0.0234)}{0.1144}\ lx_{t-1} + \underset{(0.0203)}{0.1200}\ lw_{t-1} - \underset{(0.0185)}{0.0339}\ le_{t-1} + \hat{u}_t \qquad (10.22)$$

$$R^2 = 0.47 \qquad DW = 1.94 \qquad \hat{\sigma} = 0.0192 \qquad RSS = 0.045488$$

The Ericsson and MacKinnon test can be performed by first calculating the test statistic $\tau = -0.1144 / 0.0203 = -5.63$ which is the 't-ratio' for lx_{t-1}. The 5% critical value from Ericsson and MacKinnon's response surfaces is -3.53 and therefore we reject the null and conclude that there is a cointegrating relationship between the variables.

The F-test can be performed by comparing the residual sums of square from (10.22) with that obtained when we estimate a regression equation without levels terms. Estimating the model without the levels terms produces the results given in Table 10.5. It can be noted immediately that these results mark a sharp fall in goodness of fit in that the R^2 has fallen from 0.47 in equation (10.22) to only 0.15 in this case. A more formal test can be constructed by calculating the F-statistic for the exclusion of the levels terms which is given by:

$$\Phi = \frac{0.072727 - 0.045488}{0.045488} \times \frac{130 - 6}{3} = 24.75 \qquad (10.23)$$

At this stage we need to remember that, under the null hypothesis the series are not cointegrated. Therefore the standard F-distribution is not an appropriate basis for the critical values for this test. Using Turner's response surfaces the 5% critical value in this case is 4.93 (which compares with 2.68 from the standard F distribution). Therefore we reject the null in this case even after allowing for the higher critical value.

```
Ordinary Least Squares Regression Results
Sample period: 1976.1 to 2008.2 (Quarterly Data)
Dependent Variable DLX
Sample Size 130

Variable          Coefficient        Std Err        T-Ratio

C                 -0.148488          0.074093       -2.004078
DLW                0.135731          0.032155        4.221046
DLAGX              0.012245          0.005733        2.135823

R-squared             0.1455    F-statistic         10.8148
SEE                 0.023930    RSS                0.072727
Durbin-Watson         1.2209    LogL            302.294840
ARCH(1) Test          5.0158    AIC               -4.604536
Jarque-Bera          23.4825    SIC               -4.538362
```

Table 10.5: US Export Equation without Lagged Level Terms

10.5.3 The Johansen Approach

The Johansen approach to testing for cointegration has been widely adopted in recent years. It is very difficult to give a thorough explanation of this method without a much deeper understanding of time series methods than is possible for a textbook at this level. However, we can get a reasonably intuitive understanding of the Johansen method by relating it to the error correction method.

The error-correction approach is a single equation methodology. We estimate one equation and then test for cointegration by focussing on whether the levels terms in the equation are significant. In particular, the Ericsson and MacKinnon test is based on the lagged level of the left-hand side variable. The existence of a cointegrating vector is tested for by testing the significance of the coefficient on this lag which measures the speed of adjustment when the left-hand side variable differs from its equilibrium value. Now, instead of estimating a single equation, let us consider the case in which we estimate a system of equations jointly. For example, we might have a system of two equations of the form:

$$\begin{bmatrix} \Delta X_t \\ \Delta Y_t \end{bmatrix} = \begin{bmatrix} \gamma_{11} & \gamma_{12} \\ \gamma_{21} & \gamma_{22} \end{bmatrix} \begin{bmatrix} \Delta X_{t-1} \\ \Delta Y_{t-1} \end{bmatrix} + \begin{bmatrix} \pi_{11} & \pi_{12} \\ \pi_{21} & \pi_{22} \end{bmatrix} \begin{bmatrix} X_{t-1} \\ Y_{t-1} \end{bmatrix} + \begin{bmatrix} u_{t1} \\ u_{t2} \end{bmatrix}$$

$$\text{(10.24)}$$

$$\Delta z_t = \Gamma \Delta z_{t-1} + \Pi z_{t-1} + \boldsymbol{u}_t$$

where $z_t = \begin{bmatrix} X_t & Y_t \end{bmatrix}'$.

A system of equations like this is described a *vector error correction model* or VECM since it generalises the idea of an error-correction model to a multiple equation system. Now, rather like the single equation case, if the series are not cointegrated then we would expect the levels terms on the right-hand side of this system to be insignificant when it is estimated. The Johansen test can be thought of as testing for the significance of these levels terms in much the same way as the error-correction equations do for the single equation case.

In the case of the Johansen procedure however, there are additional possibilities created by the fact that we are estimating a system of equations. In particular, it is possible that there may be more than one cointegrating vector relating the variables. The number of cointegrating vectors is tested for by testing the rank of the matrix Π. The details of the procedure through which this is done can be found in Johansen's original paper. It is enough for this account to note that there are two tests put forward based on either the trace or the maximum eigenvalue of a related matrix.

The Johansen test begins with the null hypothesis that there are no cointegrating vectors and tests this against the alternative that there is at least one. If the null is rejected, we then proceed to a second stage in which we adopt that null hypothesis that there is only one cointegrating vector and test this against the alternative that there are two or more. This process continues until we can no longer reject the null hypothesis.

Table 10.6 gives the EViews output for the Johansen test applied to our model of US exports. Both the trace test and the maximum eigenvalue tests are consistent with the existence of a single cointegrating vector.

Sample (adjusted): 1976Q2 2008Q2
Included observations: 129 after adjustments
Trend assumption: Linear deterministic trend
Series: LX LW LE
Lags interval (in first differences): 1 to 4

Unrestricted Cointegration Rank Test (Trace)

Hypothesized No. of CE(s)	Eigenvalue	Trace Statistic	0.05 Critical Value	Prob.**
None *	0.221771	38.01335	29.79707	0.0045
At most 1	0.042966	5.668604	15.49471	0.7343
At most 2	2.63E-05	0.003391	3.841466	0.9518

Trace test indicates 1 cointegrating eqn(s) at the 0.05 level
* denotes rejection of the hypothesis at the 0.05 level
**MacKinnon-Haug-Michelis (1999) p-values

Unrestricted Cointegration Rank Test (Maximum Eigenvalue)

Hypothesized No. of CE(s)	Eigenvalue	Max-Eigen Statistic	0.05 Critical Value	Prob.**
None *	0.221771	32.34475	21.13162	0.0009
At most 1	0.042966	5.665212	14.26460	0.6565
At most 2	2.63E-05	0.003391	3.841466	0.9518

Max-eigenvalue test indicates 1 cointegrating eqn(s) at the 0.05 level
* denotes rejection of the hypothesis at the 0.05 level
**MacKinnon-Haug-Michelis (1999) p-values

Table 10.6: Johansen tests for Cointegration for the US Exports Model

(EViews Output)

Exercises for Chapter 10

Exercise 1

An econometrician estimates a model relating the logarithm of the exchange rate for the US dollar and the pound to the logarithms of the UK price level and the US price level. The results obtained are as follows:

```
Ordinary Least Squares Regression Results
Sample period: 1948 to 2008 (Annual Data)
Dependent Variable LER
Sample Size 61

Variable          Coefficient        Std Err         T-Ratio

C                  0.713348         0.294390         2.423135
LPUK              -0.641630         0.123716        -5.186310
LPUS               0.579903         0.184124         3.149510

R-squared           0.8584       F-statistic        175.8760
SEE                0.104202       RSS                0.629771
Durbin-Watson      0.5139        LogL              52.929566
ARCH(1) Test      25.1455        AIC               -1.637034
Jarque-Bera       15.7743        SIC               -1.533221
```

The econometrician claims that this model is a success! A rise in UK prices causes the pound to depreciate and a rise in US price causes the pound to appreciate. Moreover, the coefficients are reasonably close to being equal and opposite in sign which indicates that it is the relative price level that matters.

You are given the task of breaking it gently to our econometrician that his results may not be as good as he thinks they are. Explain carefully why this regression equation may suffer from the spurious regression problem and point out any evidence from the estimate equation which supports your argument.

Exercise 2

Using the data in the workfile PPP.IRG, test each of the series for the presence of a unit root. If you detect unit roots, then test for the presence of a cointegrating relationship.

Exercise 3

Estimate a model which relates the same three variables, but this time use differenced data. Do your results indicate that the original regression was spurious?

Exercise 4

The workfile UK_INTEREST.IRG contains data for the yield on 20 year government bonds (R) and the Treasury Bill Rate (TBR).

a) Test each series individually to decide if they contain a unit root.

b) If the series are individually non-stationary then use the Engle-Granger test to determine if there is a cointegrating relationship between the two series.

c) Estimate an error-correction model for the bond rate (with the Treasury Bill rate on the right-hand side) and use this to construct the Ericsson and MacKinnon t-test and the F-test for cointegration.

Chapter 11: Binary Dependent Variables

11.1 Introduction

Consider the standard regression model $Y_i = \alpha + \beta X_i + u_i$. If we assume that the error follows a distribution like the normal, in which any real value is possible, then it follows that Y_i should also be able to take on any real value. However, the data we deal is often not consistent with this. In many cases the right hand side variable can only take on a limited number of values. One common example of this is where the endogenous variable is binary in nature. That is, it can take on only two values – usually zero or one. An example of this would be survey data in which individuals are asked if they are employed or unemployed. Alternatively, we might observe a sample of companies some of which go into liquidation during a given period and some of which do not. In both these cases the data can be coded so that the variable to be explained takes on two values (one for a 'success' and zero for a 'failure').

There is nothing to prevent us from calculating a least squares regression equation even if the variable to be explained is coded as a zero-one variable. However, the interpretation of such an equation becomes somewhat problematic. To illustrate this, let us consider a specific example. Suppose we have data for the share price of a particular company which is coded as 1, for days on which the share price rises, and zero, for days on which it remains constant or falls. We wish to examine whether there is a relationship between movements in the share price (coded in this way) and movements in the overall stock market index. As a first attempt at looking at this problem we estimate an OLS regression of the share price change variable (in our example this is the price of British Airways shares) on a constant and the change in the FTSE market index. The results are given in the table below:

```
Dependent Variable BA
Sample Size 1366

Variable         Coefficient         Std Err       T-Ratio

Constant            0.495899         0.012091      41.015292
FTSE               23.308994         1.249850      18.649437


R-squared           0.2032           F-statistic   347.80
SEE                 0.4466
Durbin-Watson       2.0408
ARCH(1) Test        0.3580
Jarque-Bera       129.4458
```

Table 11.1: Regression Results for British Airways Model

The results in Table 11.1 are consistent with what we might expect in that they show an apparently significant relationship between the change in the BA share price and the % change in the stock market index. This is indicated by the fact that the t-ratio for the FTSE index variable is above the 5% critical value of 1.96 by some margin. However, it is not immediately obvious how the coefficient estimate should be interpreted in this case. The FTSE variable in this case is the first difference of the logarithm of the stock market index. As such, a value of 0.01 for FTSE is equivalent to a rise of 1% in the market index. Therefore the coefficient of 23.3 indicates that a 1% rise in the overall stock market increases the expected value of the left hand side variable by 0.233 – but what does this actually mean in economic terms?

One way of interpreting the coefficients in models like this is as *marginal probabilities*. We can interpret the coefficient β as giving the increase in $P(Y_i = 1)$ associated with a unit increase in the value of X_i. In our example, the coefficient estimate of 23.3 indicates that a rise of 1% in the overall stock market increases the probability of there being an increase in the value of BA shares by 0.233. This interpretation of the regression model is referred to as the *linear probability model* because it assumes a linear relationship between the probability of an event occurring and the set of explanatory variables on the right-hand side of the estimated equation.

The linear probability model is intuitively appealing but it should quickly become apparent that this interpretation has a number of logical problems. The first concerns the nature of the probabilities estimated by the model. Since the left-hand side variable only takes on the values zero or one, the natural way to think of the data is as the outcomes of a series of Bernoulli trials or experiments which can either be 'successes' ($Y_i = 1$) or 'failures' ($Y_i = 0$). If we adopt the linear probability model interpretation of our regression then the fitted values $\hat{\alpha} + \hat{\beta}X_i$ are the estimated conditional probabilities of a success. Probability theory requires that these conditional probabilities should lie in the range zero to one since negative probabilities or probabilities greater than one make no sense. However, there is nothing in the linear probability model which constrains the conditional probabilities to lie within this range. Thus the linear probability model may easily produce nonsense results.

Examination of the actual and fitted values from our estimated model of BA share prices illustrates the inconsistency of the linear probability model. In Figure 11.1, we show the scatter of actual values against those of the right-hand side variable as well as the fitted values from the estimated regression equation. The actual values lie on two horizontal lines passing through zero and one respectively. The fitted values lie on the line with a positive slope illustrated in the diagram. For a considerable number of values of X, the fitted values fall outside the range zero to one. Out of 1,366 fitted values, 30 are less than zero and 29 are greater than one, meaning that 4.3% of the cases have estimated probabilities which lie outside the permissible range.

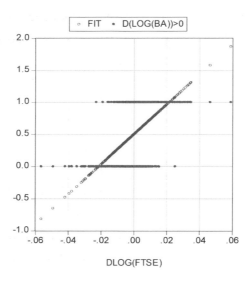

Figure 11.1: Actual and Fitted Values for the BA Share Price Model

11.2 Probit and Logit Estimation

The linear probability model has been shown to be inconsistent in that the fitted values can often fall outside the range of theoretically feasible values. However, the principle of interpreting regression results for a model with a binary dependent variable as giving estimates of probabilities remains a promising approach. What we need to do is to find and alternative formulation which does not suffer from the inconsistencies of the linear probability framework. In fact there are a number of possible solutions to this problem which we will now consider.

Let us begin by assuming that we can find a function of X which gives the probability that Y is equal to one i.e. we need a function $g(X_i) = P(Y_i = 1 | X_i)$. Note that it immediately follows that $P(Y_i = 0 | X_i) = 1 - g(X_i)$ This function should have the following properties: (1) the probability show always lie between the values 0 and 1 for any value of X, (2) the probability that $Y = 1$ should approach zero for very small values of X and (3) the

236

probability that $Y = 1$ should approach one for very large values of X. Now, assuming that we can find a function which has these properties, we can write down the joint probability of observing any particular set of values of Y as:

$$\prod_{i=1}^{N} g(X_i)^{Y_i} \left(1 - g(X_i)\right)^{1-Y_i} \tag{11.1}$$

The function $g(X_i)$ will typically depend on a number of parameters. For example, if we take the linear probability function then we would have $g(X_i) = \alpha + \beta X_i$. Suppose we write the function in terms of its parameters as $g(X_i | \alpha, \beta)$, then we can substitute this into the joint probability function to obtain the likelihood function:

$$L(\alpha, \beta) = \prod_{i=1}^{N} g(\alpha, \beta | X_i)^{Y_i} \left(1 - g(\alpha, \beta | X_i)\right)^{1-Y_i} \tag{11.2}$$

or, taking logarithms of (11.2) we have the log-likelihood function:

$$LL(\alpha, \beta) = \sum_{i=1}^{N} Y_i \ln\left(g(\alpha, \beta | X_i)\right) + (1 - Y_i) \ln\left(1 - g(\alpha, \beta | X_i)\right) \tag{11.3}$$

The method of *maximum likelihood* involves choosing estimated values of the parameters $\hat{\alpha}$ and $\hat{\beta}$ which maximise the function defined above in equation (11.3). In most cases it will not be possible to find an analytical solution for the maximum likelihood estimator. However, it will usually be possible to use numerical methods to find estimates of the unknown parameters.

Now, let us consider a particular functional form for the probability as shown in equation (11.4). This is known as the *logistic* function:

$$g(X_i) = \frac{\exp(\alpha + \beta X_i)}{1 + \exp(\alpha + \beta X_i)} \qquad\qquad (11.4)$$

$$\alpha := 0 \qquad\qquad \beta := 1$$

$$g(x) := \frac{\exp(\alpha + \beta \cdot x)}{1 + \exp(\alpha + \beta \cdot x)}$$

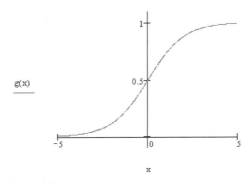

$g(x)$

Figure 11.2: The Logistic Function

Does this have reasonable properties for a probability function? The plot of equation (11.4) shown in Figure 11.2 indicates that this is in fact a reasonable functional form. From Figure 11.2 we see that it has the following properties. First, $g(X_i) > 0$ for any value of X, second we have $\lim_{X \to -\infty} g(X) = 0$ and third we have $\lim_{X \to \infty} g(X_i) = 1$. Thus (11.4) satisfies all the criteria for a reasonable probability function. Given this probability function, the maximum likelihood estimator can be found as:

$$\arg\max \sum_{i=1}^{N} Y_i \ln\left(\frac{\exp(\hat{\alpha} + \hat{\beta} X_i)}{1 + \exp(\hat{\alpha} + \hat{\beta} X_i)} \right) + (1 - Y_i)\ln\left(\frac{1}{1 + \exp(\hat{\alpha} + \hat{\beta} X_i)} \right) \qquad (11.5)$$

Although we cannot find an analytical solution to this problem, it is relatively easy to find a numerical solution. For example, using our data set for the returns on British Airways shares, we obtain the following results:

```
Logit Estimates
Newton-Raphson Method

Dependent Variable BA
Sample Size 1366
Iterations 5

Variable         Coefficient        Std Err        T-Ratio

Constant          -0.042613        0.061751       -0.690081
FTSE             148.920724       10.112424       14.726511

Mean of RHS Variable     0.30158863e-3
SDev of RHS Variable     0.30169908e-3
Log Likelihood           -770.4887
Restricted LogL          -946.8156
McFadden R-Squared        0.186232
Marginal Effect          37.158969
```

Table 11.2: Estimates of the Logistic Probability model for BA Share Prices

The estimates in Table 11.2 indicate that the percentage change in the FTSE index has a significant effect on the probability of a rise in the value of British Airways shares. Moreover, this effect is positive with a rise in the market as a whole increasing the probability of a rise in BA shares. It is difficult however, to interpret the regression results in more detail without more work. This is because the estimated slope coefficient does not measure a marginal effect in the same way as that for the linear probability model. In the case of the linear probability model we can read off the marginal effect directly from the value of the coefficient. The slope coefficient of 23.3 indicates that a 1% increase in the value of the stock market (an increase of 0.01) increases the probability of a rise in BA share value by 0.233. Unfortunately, such a straightforward interpretation of the slope coefficient is not possible when we consider the logistic regression.

To interpret the slope coefficient of the logistic regression, let us consider once again the interpretation of the equation we have estimated. The parameters of the estimated equation determine the shape of the probability function. That is the estimated probability of the variable Y being equal to one is given by the formula:

$$P(Y_i = 1) = \frac{\exp(\hat{\alpha} + \hat{\beta}X_i)}{1 + \exp(\hat{\alpha} + \hat{\beta}X_i)} \qquad (11.6)$$

How does the value of $\hat{\beta}$ affect this probability? If we differentiate (11.6) with respect to $\hat{\beta}$ then we have:

$$\frac{\partial P(Y_i = 1)}{\partial \hat{\beta}} = \frac{\hat{\beta}}{\left(1 + \exp(\hat{\alpha} + \hat{\beta}X_i)\right)^2} \qquad (11.7)$$

This shows that the marginal effect on the probability is a decreasing function of the right-hand side variable X. In order to get some idea of the size of the marginal effect we can evaluate (11.7) at the same mean of X. In this case we have

$$\frac{\hat{\beta}}{\left(1 + \exp(\hat{\alpha} + \hat{\beta}\bar{X})\right)^2} = \frac{148.92}{\left(1 + \exp(-0.0426 + 148.92 \times 0.0003015)\right)^2}$$
$$= 37.15$$

Again we can express this in more meaningful terms by considering the effect of a 1% rise in the value of stock market. In this case such a shock would increase the probability of an increase in the BA share price by an amount given by $37.15 \times 0.01 = 0.3715$

The assessment of goodness of fit is more difficult in models with binary dependent variables. How, for example, do we even compare a fitted value from such a regression with the actual values which can only take on the values zero or one? One method of calculating goodness of fit is to compare the log-likelihood when we allow for the influence of the exogenous variable X from that when we assume that the probability that y is equal to one does not dependent on X. We will describe this latter probability as the 'naive' probability. The naive probability will be determined by a single parameter α and we can obtain an estimate of this parameter using exactly the same maximum likelihood procedure which we have described already for the more general model. Let $\tilde{c}$ be the maximum likelihood estimator of the naive probability. From our results we have $LL(\tilde{c}$ 8156 which is clearly lower than the log-likelihood when we allow x to affect the probability which is given by $LL(\hat{\alpha},\hat{\beta})=-770.4887$. If we calculate $1-LL(\hat{\alpha},\hat{\beta})/LL(\tilde{c}$ then we obtain McFadden's R^2 measure for a model with a limited dependent variable. This has the standard properties of R^2 in that it has an expected value of 0 when the X variable has no predictive value and is bounded above by 1 at which the X variable would become a perfect predictor of the Y variable. In this case the McFadden's R^2 can be calculated as:

$$\text{McFadden } R^2 = 1 - \frac{-770.4887}{-946.8156} = 0.186$$

This indicates that, while the change in the FTSE index does provide some explanatory power, it is far from a perfect predictor and that there are other, company specific, factors which are responsible for movements in the price of BA shares.

11.3 An Aside on Maximum Likelihood

The method of maximum likelihood comes into its own when dealing with limited dependent variable models. However, it is a technique which can be applied in a much broader set of circumstances and it is interesting to look at it in more detail.

Maximum likelihood begins with assumption that we can specify a probability density function for some linear combination of the variables of interest. For example, in the simple regression model we might start with the assumption that the errors

$u_i = Y_i - \alpha - \beta X_i$ follow a normal distribution with mean zero and variance σ^2 and that they are independent of each other. Let us write the PDF of the errors as $f(u_i)$. The joint probability of the observed sample of data can be written:

$$\prod_{i=1}^{N} f(u_1) \times f(u_2) \times f(u_3) \ldots f(u_N) \tag{11.8}$$

Now if we view (11.8) in the conventional manner, it consists of a function of the sample data $(Y_i, X_i); i = 1, \ldots N$ for given values of the parameters α, β and σ^2. As such this defines the joint probability of observing the data which we actually do observe. However, there is another way of looking at (11.8). This is to view it as a function of α, β and σ^2 for a given set of data. This interpretation of the function is referred to as the *likelihood function* and it forms the basis for the method of maximum likelihood estimation. Let us write the likelihood function as $L(\alpha, \beta, \sigma^2)$. The maximum likelihood estimator (MLE) of the parameters of this model is defined as the values $\hat{\alpha}$, $\hat{\beta}$ and $\hat{\sigma}^2$ which satisfy the first order conditions for a maximum of the likelihood function i.e.

$$\frac{\partial L(\alpha, \beta, \sigma^2)}{\partial \alpha} = \frac{\partial L(\alpha, \beta, \sigma^2)}{\partial \beta} = \frac{\partial L(\alpha, \beta, \sigma^2)}{\partial \sigma^2} = 0 \tag{11.9}$$

In practice we more often use the logarithm of likelihood function which will give the same answer (by virtue of the fact that the maximum is not affected by a monotonic transformation of the function) with rather less effort.

The maximum likelihood method is often introduced in textbooks by assuming a normal distribution. This is partly because it is relatively easy to derive analytical solutions for the estimator in this case and partly because it can then be compared with the least squares estimator. This does not do justice to the power of the maximum likelihood approach which can be applied to a very much broader range of problems. Indeed, providing we can specify an appropriate PDF, the maximum likelihood approach can cover just about any problem of interest for the applied econometrician. However, this power does not come without some difficulties. In many situations we cannot derive an analytical solution for the MLE, even when the PDF is known and reasonably tractable. This means that we often make use of numerical methods to solve for maximum likelihood estimates. To calculate the variances of the maximum likelihood estimates we use the matrix of second derivatives of the log-likelihood function.

11.4 Some alternative limited dependent variable estimators

In order to deal with the binary dependent variable we have so far made use of the logit model. That is we have assumed that the probability that the right-hand side variable is equal to one can be written in terms of the formula $P(Y_i = 1) = \exp(\alpha + \beta X_i)/1 + \exp(\alpha + \beta X_i)$. The problem is then one of using an appropriate estimation technique to estimate the unknown parameters α and β. The choice of the logit function was made simply on the basis that it has a number of properties which make it suitable for a probability function. These include the properties that it is always positive, always lies between zero and one, approaches zero as $X \rightarrow -\infty$ and approaches one as $X \rightarrow \infty$. However, the logit function is by no means the only functional form which has these properties and there are a number of other possible functions which might be employed to model the probability that y is equal to one. We will consider two alternatives. These are the *probit model* and the *extreme value model*.

The probit model is based on the cumulative distribution function for the normal distribution. If we consider the function:

$$\Phi(\alpha + \beta X_i) = \int_{-\infty}^{\alpha + \beta X_i} \phi(s) ds \qquad (11.10)$$

where $\phi(\ )$ is the probability density function of the normal distribution, then it is easy to see that (11.10) has all the desirable properties for a function which describes $P(Y_i = 1)$. Moreover, although (11.10) looks quite forbidding, the normal distribution is such a well known distribution that calculation of the probabilities implied by it are quite straightforward (though again will require numerical methods. Therefore we can again use maximum likelihood methods to obtain estimates $\hat{\alpha}$ and $\hat{\beta}$ of the unknown parameters α and β.

If we apply the probit model to the same sample of data used to construct the logit estimates given in Table 11.2 then we obtain the following results.

```
Probit Estimates
Newton-Raphson Method

Dependent Variable BA
Sample Size 1366
Iterations 5

Variable        Coefficient        Std Err         T-Ratio

Constant         -0.025001        0.037129        -0.673346
FTSE             88.071855        5.569184        15.814140

Mean of RHS Variable     0.30158863e-3
SDev of RHS Variable     0.30169908e-3
Log Likelihood           -770.8716
Restricted LogL          -946.8156
McFadden R-Squared        0.185827
Marginal Effect          43.981096
```

Table 11.3 Estimates of the Probit model for BA Share Prices

Although the coefficients of the probit model look very different from those of the logit model, the differences are, in fact very small. What we need to remember is that these coefficients are parameters of the relevant likelihood functions and that the functional forms assumed are quite different. However, in terms of the accuracy with which the models fit the data, they are remarkably similar. This can be seen through the McFadden R^2 values which in both cases take a value of just over 0.18. This indicates that each model increases the value of the log likelihood by a factor of about 18% relative to the naive model. Moreover, we can again evaluate the marginal effect of the right hand side variable on $P(Y_i = 1)$ at its mean value as:

$$\frac{\partial P(Y_i = 1)}{\partial X_i} = \phi(\hat{\alpha}, \hat{\beta}, \bar{X})\hat{\beta} = 35.136 \qquad (11.11)$$

This is very close to the value of 37.15 which we obtained for the logit model. Therefore both the goodness of fit statistics and the marginal effects indicate that both models are telling us essentially the same story. This can be confirmed by examination of the extent to which these models accurately predict the direction of movements of BA shares. In Table 11.4 below we show the predictions of each model. These predictions have been calculated on the based that if the fitted values of the probabilities lie above 0.5 then we predict $Y=1$ and it the fitted probabilities are less than or equal to 0.5 then we predict $Y=0$. There are four possible outcomes which are listed below:

Case 1	$\hat{P} > 0.5$ $Y=1$	Prediction correct
Case 2	$\hat{P} \leq 0.5$ $Y=1$	Prediction incorrect
Case 3	$\hat{P} > 0.5$ $Y=0$	Prediction incorrect
Case 4	$\hat{P} \leq 0.5$ $Y=0$	Prediction correct

The success of the model depends on the proportion of Case 1 and Case 4 outcomes it succeeds in achieving. We can evaluate the contribution of the X variable as a predictor of Y by comparing the proportion of correct predictions from the full model with those of the naive model which excludes the X variable. If the inclusion of the X variable produces increases in Case 1 and Case 4 outcomes, while reducing Case 2 and Case 3 outcomes, then X provides useful information in predicting the value of the left hand side variable. For the logit and probit models we have estimated, we obtain the following results.

Logit Model

	Y=1	Y=0
P> 0.50	0.36	0.15
	(0.11)	(-0.10)
P< 0.50	0.14	0.34
	(-0.11)	(0.09)

Probit Model

	Y=1	Y=0
P> 0.50	0.36	0.15
	(0.11)	(-0.10)
P< 0.50	0.14	0.34
	(-0.11)	(0.09)

Table 11.4: Predictions of the Logit and Probit models

We can see from Table 11.4 that the logit and probit models actually produce identical results. In each case the proportion of correct predictions is 70% which compares with 50% from the naive model.[6]

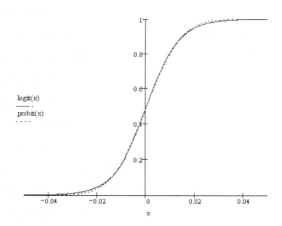

Figure 11.3 Logit and Probit Functions for Estimated Models

---

[6] The 50% success rate of the naive model reflects the roughly even distribution of increases and decreases in the value of BA shares over the sample period. Prediction with the naive model is more or less equivalent to deciding whether the share value will rise or fall on the basis of the toss of a coin.

The essential similarity of the logit and probit models can also be seen by plotting probability functions for the values of the estimated parameters. These functions are shown in Figure 11.1 which illustrates how similar are the results of the two models. For values of X in the middle of its range, there is virtually no difference between the two functions. The difference between the two functions tends to get a little larger for more extreme values of X.

A third function which has been applied to the analysis of limited dependent variables is the *extreme value* which is also known as the *Gompit* or *Weibull* distribution. The functional form for the probability in this case can be written as:

$$P(Y_i = 1) = \exp\left(-\exp\left(-(\alpha + \beta X_i)\right)\right) \qquad (11.12)$$

This can also be shown to have the desirable properties for a probability distribution that $P(Y_i = 1) >$ for all values of X, that $P(Y_i = 1) \to 0$ as $X \to -\infty$ and that $P(Y_i = 1) \to 1$ as $X \to \infty$. This function differs from the logit and probit functions in being *asymmetric*. Consider the case in which $\alpha + \beta X_i = 0$. In the case of the logit and probit functions we have $P(Y_i = 1 | \alpha + \beta X_i = 0) = P(Y_i = 0 | \alpha + \beta X_i = 0) = 0.5$. That is the probabilities are evenly distributed around $\alpha + \beta X_i = 0$. However, this is not the case for the extreme value function where $P(Y_i = 1 | \alpha + \beta X_i = 0) = 0.3679$. This indicates that 'successes' ($Y=1$) are less likely that 'failures' ($Y=0$) with the extreme value model. With that in mind we would expect the results of this model to differ somewhat from the logit and probit results. When we estimate our model for BA share prices using the extreme value distribution then we obtain the following results:

```
Extreme Value Estimates
Newton-Raphson Method

Dependent Variable BA
Sample Size 1366
Iterations 6

Variable        Coefficient       Std Err        T-Ratio

Constant          0.402378       0.043233        9.307189
FTSE             94.917960       5.783424       16.412071

Mean of RHS Variable    0.30158863e-3
SDev of RHS Variable    0.30169908e-3
Log Likelihood          -774.5504
Restricted LogL         -946.8156
McFadden R-Squared      0.181942
```

Table 11.5 Estimates of the extreme value model for BA Share Prices

In fact, the extreme value method results indicate a very similar effect on the log-likelihood, with the McFadden R^2 again reaching a value of about 0.18. However, the table of outcomes for this model is somewhat different as shown in Table 11.6. The total success rate of this model is slightly higher with the proportion of correct predictions for $y=1$ increasing by 2% relative to the logit and probit models, although the proportion of correct predictions of $y=0$ falls by 1%.

```
                  Extreme Value Model
                       Y=1              Y=0

        P> 0.50        0.38             0.17
                     ( 0.13)          (-0.08)
        P< 0.50        0.12             0.33
                     (-0.13)          ( 0.07)
```

Exercises for Chapter 11

Exercise 1

Using the data in the workfile CADB.IRG, estimate the linear probability model and the logit model relating the direction of movement of Cadbury-Schweppes shares to the change in the value of the stock market. Explain the meaning of the slope coefficient in each case and intepret your results.

Exercise 2

Using the data in the workfile CADB.IRG, estimate logit, probit and extreme value models for the direction of movement of Cadbury-Schweppes shares. Assess which of these provides the best predictor of the endogenous variable.

References

Abadir, Karim M. and Magnus, Jan R. (2002) "Notation in econometrics: a proposal for a standard", *Econometrics Journal*, Vol 5, pp. 76-90.

Dickey, D. A. and Fuller, W. A. (1979) "Distribution of the estimators for autoregressive time series with a unit root", *Journal of the American Statistical Association*, 74, pp. 427-31.

Ericsson, N., and MacKinnon, J., (2002) "Distributions of error correction tests for cointegration", *Econometrics Journal*, 5, pp. 251-276.

Gilbert, C. L. (1986) "Professor Hendry"s econometric methodology", *Oxford Bulletin of Economics and Statistics*, 48, pp. 283-307.

Granger, C.W.J and Newbold, P. (1974) "Spurious regressions in econometrics", *Journal of Econometrics*, 2, pp. 111-20.

Greene, W. H. (1993) *Econometric Analysis*, 2nd edn, Macmillan, New York.

Hendry, D. and Mizon, G. (1978) "Serial correlation as a convenient simplification, not a nuisance: a comment on a study of the demand for money by the Bank of England", *Economic Journal*, 88, pp. 549-563.

Johansen, S., (1988) "Statistical analysis of cointegrating vectors", *Journal of Economic Dynamics and Control*, 12, pp. 231-254.

MacKinnon, J.G. (1991) "Critical Values for Cointegration Tests", in Engle, R.F. and Granger, C.W.J. (eds) *Long-Run Economic Relationships*, Oxford: Oxford University Press.

MacKinnon, James G., Alfred A. Haug, and Leo Michelis (1999), "Numerical Distribution Functions of Likelihood Ratio Tests For Cointegration," *Journal of Applied Econometrics*, 14, 563-577.

Nelson, C. R. and Plosser, C. I. (1992) "Trends and random walks in macroeconomic time series: some evidence and implications", *Journal of Monetary Economics*, 10, 139-62.

Pesaran, M.H., Shin, Y. and Smith, R.J. (2000) "Structural analysis of vector error correction model with exogenous I(1) variables", *Journal of Econometrics*, 97, 293-343.

Turner, P. (2006) "Response Surfaces for an F-Test for Cointegration", *Applied Economics Letters*, 13(8), June, pp. 279-282.

White, H. (1980) "A Heteroskedasticity-Consistent Covariance Matrix Estimator and a Direct Test for Heteroskedasticity", *Econometrica*, 50, pp.1-25.

INDEX